This

JOURNAL

belongs to:

_____

Thank you for purchasing
MY BASKETBALL JOURNAL
52 weeks of goals, growth, and gratitude.

It is my genuine hope that this journal can help you grow as a person and a basketball player.

Love what you do! Do what you love!

Please share your story with me
through email or social media.
Email me at srfabricoauthor@gmail.com,
and I will send you a free inspirational coloring page.

For bulk discount orders, email srfabricoauthor@gmail.com

Let's get social!

@srfabricoauthor @myjournalseries

@srfabrico_author @the_myjournalseries

@srfabrico_author

S.R. Fabrico

srfabricoauthor@gmail.com

srfabrico.com

MY BASKETBALL JOURNAL

52 weeks of goals, growth, and gratitude

S.R. Fabrico

Copyright © 2022 S. R. Fabrico All rights reserved.

This book contains material protected under international and federal copyright laws and treaties. Any unauthorized report or use of this material is prohibited. No part of this book may be reproduced or transmitted in any form or by any means, electronic or mechanical, including photocopying, recording, or by any information storage and retrieval system without express written permission from the author/publisher.

Mentions of public figures in this book do not imply endorsement by the author or publisher. The information in this book should not be treated as a substitute for medical advice. Neither the author nor publisher can be held responsible for any loss, claim, or damage from the use, misuse, or suggestions made in the contents within this book. In event you use any information in this book for yourself, the author and the publisher assume no responsibility for your actions.

PAPERBACK ISBN: 978-1-962546-00-3
HARDBACK ISBN: 978-1-962546-01-0

Published by: SRF Creations

For Big Jon.

Thanks for being an incredible role model for your son,
my husband.
Keep shooting those heavenly hoops.

TABLE OF CONTENTS

NOTE FROM THE AUTHOR	1
AFFIRMATIONS	5
HOW TO USE THIS JOURNAL	6
Goal Setting	6
Accomplishments I am proud of	7
How I Helped My Teammates	7
Favorite Basketball Moments	8
Hydration	8
Monthly Reflection	9
Video Review Notes	9
Why I Am Grateful	9
Thank You	9
GOAL SETTING TIPS	10
VISION BOARD	10
GOALS FOR THE YEAR	12
QUARTERLY BENCHMARK GOALS	13
BEGIN YOUR WEEKLY JOURNALING	14
SEASON STATS AND MEMORIES	161
ACKNOWLEDGMENTS	172
ABOUT THE AUTHOR	173
SUBSCRIBE	174
OTHER WORKS BY THE AUTHOR	175

NOTE FROM THE AUTHOR

Congratulations! You fell in love with basketball. That's awesome! Basketball can be rewarding and exciting. Losing yourself on the court is one of the best feelings in the world. As you train and prepare for your games and tournaments, remember to go back to the court and just have fun.

Throughout your basketball journey, you will have many ups and downs. Embrace them. There will be days when you don't enjoy training, or your coaches are pushing you harder than you like. These feelings are part of the journey. They are part of growth. Just like your body experiences growing pains that hurt, so do your thinking and emotions. Journaling your steps along the way can help remind you of the roadblocks, accomplishments, and successful moments.

You will sometimes struggle to be the fastest to the ball. Once again, these hurdles are part of the journey. There will be times when you don't make the team you want or don't get chosen for the position you want. These setbacks are all part of your journey. Basketball is WHAT you do; basketball does not define WHO you are!

Who you are is how you treat yourself and others. Be kind to yourself. Have faith and confidence in the journey. Do the work to achieve your goals, and eventually, you will succeed. Be someone upon whom your teammates and basketball friends rely. They are going through the same journey and share a lot of your fears.

Be coachable! This concept is important. Your coaches aren't criticizing you because they don't like you. They do like you and want to help you grow. Listen to them and be grateful for the constructive feedback that will make you a better basketball player. If you are lucky enough to have an excellent coach, she or he will also help you be a better person.

Know that you are going to make mistakes along the way. Mistakes are 100% OKAY! Mistakes are how you learn, so forgive yourself. Capitalize on your mistakes to do better in the future. Forgive others for their mistakes. Remember that not everyone will be kind. Attitude is part of life and part of learning. Over time, you will know that you cannot control how others act and react, but you can control your actions and reactions. Treat others as you want to be treated and work every day to be the best basketball player and person you can be. I hope this basketball journal will help you to cherish the memories. I hope you will reflect after your season and see that you accomplished many goals, grew as a person and a basketball player, and believe how exceptional you are!

Always be YOU-niquely YOU!

Much Love,
STACY

YOU CAN DO ANYTHING YOU PUT YOUR MIND TO.

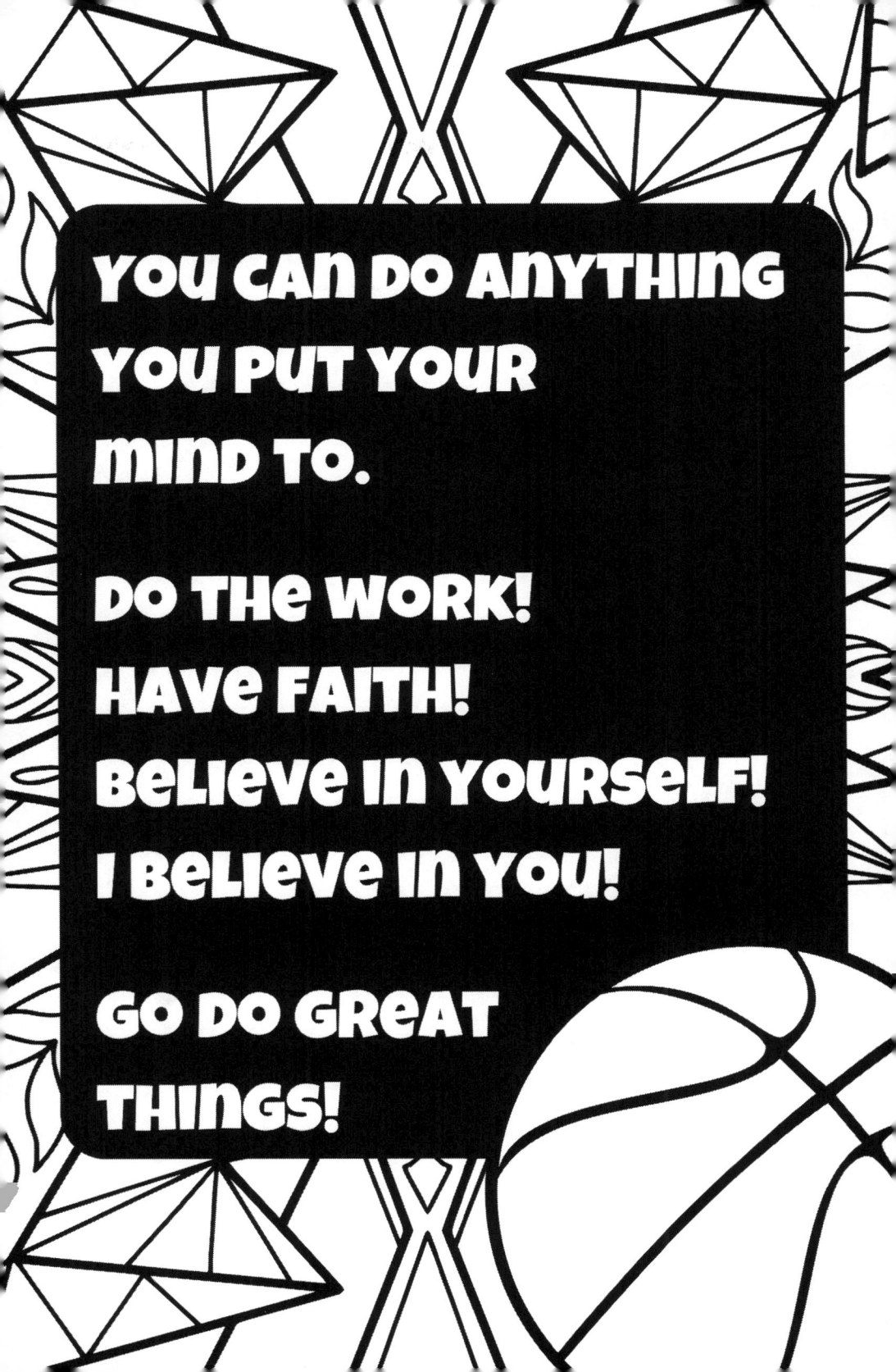

DO THE WORK!
HAVE FAITH!
BELIEVE IN YOURSELF!
I BELIEVE IN YOU!

GO DO GREAT THINGS!

SUCCESS IS NO ACCIDENT

IT IS HARD WORK

AFFIRMATIONS

I am a good teammate.
I set goals, and I reach them.
I am a good basketball player.
I am proud to be me.
I take pride in my progress.
I make the most of each moment.
I am proud of what I have accomplished.
I am hardworking.
I am dedicated.
My potential is limitless.
I feel good about myself.
I feel good about my body.
I have a purpose.
Who I am makes a difference.
I am in charge of my success.
I can accomplish anything.
I take pride in my work.
I am courageous.
I am confident.
I love myself.
I am strong.
I am resilient.
I am capable.
I am kind.
I am smart.
I am worthy.
I am enough.
I am unique.
I am valuable.

HOW TO USE THIS JOURNAL
RECORD YOUR PROGRESS

GOAL SETTING

Setting goals for yourself is essential to your success if you want to continue growing and learning. Goals are milestones or achievements along the way. The cool thing about goals is understanding that even if you don't reach every goal, you grew while pursuing your goals, and that is what matters most.

At the beginning of this journal, you will set significant goals that you want to accomplish by the end of your basketball season. You will then set quarterly benchmark goals. You can achieve your benchmark goals in short periods of time. Benchmark goals keep you on track to achieve your year-end goal. Each month you will set monthly goals that are baby steps along your journey.

Let's recap for clarity one more time!

- What are my significant goals for the season?
- How can I set myself up for success in order to reach those goals?
- What are my quarterly benchmark goals?
- What monthly goals can I set to push me in the right direction along my journey?

Set your monthly goals at the beginning of each month with your quarterly goals in mind. For example, let's say one of your yearly goals is to increase your speed and dribbling skills. Set a quarterly goal to shave a specific amount of seconds off your time running 400 meters. Your monthly goals may be to practice dribbling with your left hand, run four times a week, do core strengthening exercises daily, and remind yourself daily that you can achieve your goal. These are goals you choose. Again, break down your significant goals into bite-size goals.

Now, let's set some goals!

ACCOMPLISHMENTS I AM PROUD OF

Each week jot down your small wins for the week. It is essential to document small victories along the way. They remind you of the work you put in each week. These accomplishments may be physical growth or mental growth, like keeping a positive attitude all week. Perhaps getting enough rest or drinking plenty of water each day improved. Whatever makes YOU proud and feel good, write it down; you will appreciate it when you look back later. No accomplishment is too small.

HOW I HELPED MY TEAMMATES

You rise by lifting others. The fantastic benefit of being part of a team or group is that you have other people working to achieve the same goals. You may have team goals to consider in your journey, so think about those goals when planning. What are you doing to help your team succeed? Also, consider how you are contributing to your teammates' individual successes. We all need someone to cheer us on and root for us if we feel down or don't want to do the extra work

How are you contributing to your team culture? Are you a negative apple that sours the bunch, or are you a light that shines as an example to those around you? What kind of teammate do you want to be?

In this journal section, you can jot down both the good and the bad. News flash: no one is perfect—not even you. You are meant only to be perfectly unique. Maybe one week you're the negative apple, and the next week you're the shining light. THAT'S OKAY! Don't be afraid to spread compliments to those around you. Tell them if they are doing well, crushing a practice, or improving their game play.

Acknowledge your teammates' success! Write about it! Determine how YOU can contribute to helping those around you rise. Sometimes you need help from others to help you grow, which is OKAY too!

HYDRATION

Each day, you can choose to hold yourself accountable by marking down how many glasses of water you've had for the day. Your body needs water, period. Water hydrates your skin, and it can help with your digestion. Water helps boost your energy and provides fuel to your muscles. As a basketball player, you need the proper fuel for your body to function correctly. You are consistently working out and pushing your body to reach new heights daily. Treat yourself right and drink plenty of water. Fruits and veggies are good too, but we will save that topic for another day.

VIDEO REVIEW NOTES

Watch game footage and assess yourself with honest eyes. Make note of great plays by others too. What did you and your team do well, and where could you improve? There is much to be learned from watching your games.

REFLECTION

The reflection page is an opportunity for you to look back on the month. Where did you succeed? Where could you do better? Who impacted your month? Who did you impact? This page offers a moment to think back, write notes, and grow.

WHY I AM GRATEFUL

Have an attitude of gratitude. Research shows that gratitude is associated with greater happiness. Use this page to jot down what you are most grateful for throughout the month in your life, basketball, or school. Express your gratitude to others.

THANK YOU

Write notes to people who impacted you during the last month. You can keep the notes private or send them. Either way, it is good to write down your thanks and remember who helped you along your journey.

GOAL SETTING TIPS

Set SMART goals
- Specific - Make sure your goals are well defined.
- Measurable - Consider how you will measure the achievement of your goals. ·For example, if your goal is to improve your ball control. How will you determine if your ball control has improved?
- Achievable - You want to set goals that are realistic.
- Relevant - If you are on a basketball team a relevant goal might be to increae your free-throw percentage. Setting a goal to learn how to kick a football through the goal post isn't going to help you as a basketball player. However, I would consider this a fun goal. You can set some "fun" goals, but understand how these goals won't impact your team or your basketball specific goals.
- Time focused - Set a deadline to achieve your goals.

Lucky for you, your My Basketball Journal helps you to set SMART goals.

VISION BOARD

A vision board is anything that inspires you. You can draw, doodle, cut and paste pictures or quotes. Choose things that you want to be, feel or do. Allow your mind to see yourself inside your vision board. For example, perhaps you want to be an NBA Player. You might draw images that represent the NBA or paste pictures of your favorite NBA players. Maybe you want to play basketball at a specific college or university. Fill up your vision board with images or words that represent your chosen school. Perhaps you want to make a semi-pro team. I think you get the point now. There is no wrong way to do a vision board. It's yours, so have fun!

VISION BOARD

GOALS FOR THE YEAR

PERSONAL GOALS

TEAM GOALS

ACADEMIC GOALS

QUARTERLY BENCHMARK GOALS

PERSONAL GOALS

TEAM GOALS

ACADEMIC GOALS

GOALS FOR THE MONTH

PERSONAL GOALS

TEAM GOALS

ACADEMIC GOALS

WEEK:_____   DATE:_____/_____/_____

HYDRATION

Week 1

Week 2

Week 3

Week 4

WEEK:_____ DATE:_____ / _____ / _____

Below is an example of how to fill out the weekly pages.

ACCOMPLISHMENTS I'M PROUD OF
I was able to send an accurate

pass under pressure today!

HOW I HELPED MY TEAMMATES
Josh was struggling with conditioning and I went over and

cheered for him, then decided to do it with him even

though I had finsihed mine already

FAVORITE BASKETBALL MOMENTS
My favorite moment was when coach Cap told me that

he was proud of my effort and I would start the game

GETTING BUCKETS - PRACTICE NOTES AND AT-HOME GOALS
Remind mom that i need to pay ref fees

SHOOTING   100 free throws 3/wk

DRIBBLING   weak hand 30 min 3X/wk

SPRINTS   10 - 3X/wk

DISTANCE RUN   1 mile - 2/wk

WEEK:_____   DATE:_____/_____/_____

Start each day with a grateful heart, and you will be fulfilled.

ACCOMPLISHMENTS I'M PROUD OF
_____
_____
_____

HOW I HELPED MY TEAMMATES
_____
_____
_____

FAVORITE BASKETBALL MOMENTS
_____
_____
_____

GETTING BUCKETS - PRACTICE NOTES AND AT-HOME GOALS
_____
_____

SHOOTING _____ ☐

DRIBBLING _____ ☐

SPRINTS   _____ ☐

DISTANCE RUN _____ ☐

WEEK:_____   DATE:_____/_____/_____

Failures are learning opportunities along the way to success.

ACCOMPLISHMENTS I'M PROUD OF
_____
_____
_____

HOW I HELPED MY TEAMMATES
_____
_____
_____

FAVORITE BASKETBALL MOMENTS
_____
_____
_____

GETTING BUCKETS - PRACTICE NOTES AND AT-HOME GOALS
_____
_____

SHOOTING   _____ ☐

DRIBBLING   _____ ☐

SPRINTS   _____ ☐

DISTANCE RUN _____ ☐

WEEK:_____   DATE:_____/_____/_____

Cherish the time with teammates and friends.

ACCOMPLISHMENTS I'M PROUD OF
_____
_____
_____

HOW I HELPED MY TEAMMATES
_____
_____
_____
_____

FAVORITE BASKETBALL MOMENTS
_____
_____
_____
_____

GETTING BUCKETS - PRACTICE NOTES AND AT-HOME GOALS
_____
_____

SHOOTING _____ ☐

DRIBBLING _____ ☐

SPRINTS _____ ☐

DISTANCE RUN _____ ☐

WEEK:_____   DATE:_____/_____/_____

Make sure to eat your fruits and veggies.

ACCOMPLISHMENTS I'M PROUD OF
_____
_____
_____

HOW I HELPED MY TEAMMATES
_____
_____
_____

FAVORITE BASKETBALL MOMENTS
_____
_____
_____

GETTING BUCKETS - PRACTICE NOTES AND AT-HOME GOALS
_____
_____

SHOOTING   _____   ☐
DRIBBLING   _____   ☐
SPRINTS   _____   ☐
DISTANCE RUN _____   ☐

WEEK:_____   DATE:_____/_____/_____

CELEBRATE MONTHLY PRACTICE WINS

Practice wins don't always have to be about learning new skills. Wins could be that you welcomed newcomers to your team and made them feel comfortable at a new club. Wins could be that you stayed positive even though you were having a hard day. Celebrating EVERY win is crucial to success and growth!

HOW DID MY SKILLS GROW?

_____
_____
_____
_____

HOW DID MY CHARACTER GROW?

_____
_____
_____

HOW DID I GROW MENTALLY?

_____
_____
_____

AFFIRMATIONS IN ACTION - visualize my goals as I say the statements below out loud.

When I did my _____, I felt _____
When my team _____, I felt _____

WEEK:_____   DATE:_____/_____/_____

MONTHLY REFLECTION

Self-Reflection is looking back so that looking forward can be even clearer.

DID I REACH MY GOALS? If yes, what steps did I take to reach my goals? If not, what could I have done differently?

_____
_____
_____
_____

I WAS MOST POSITIVELY IMPACTED BY...

_____
_____
_____
_____

I POSITIVELY IMPACTED...

_____
_____
_____
_____

IN THE COMING WEEKS, I AM LOOKING FORWARD TO...

_____
_____
_____
_____

WEEK:_____   DATE:_____/_____/_____

VIDEO REVIEW NOTES

SUCCESSFUL MOMENTS WITHOUT THE BALL
_____
_____

SUCCESSFUL MOMENTS WITH THE BALL
_____
_____

MOMENTS I'D LIKE TO IMPROVE UPON
_____
_____

EFFORT LEVEL (1-5, 1 being the best effort)
Beginning _____ Middle _____ End _____

SUCCESSFUL MOMENTS WITHOUT THE BALL
_____
_____

SUCCESSFUL MOMENTS WITH THE BALL
_____
_____

MOMENTS I'D LIKE TO IMPROVE UPON
_____
_____

EFFORT LEVEL (1-5, 1 being the highest)
Beginning _____ Middle _____ End _____

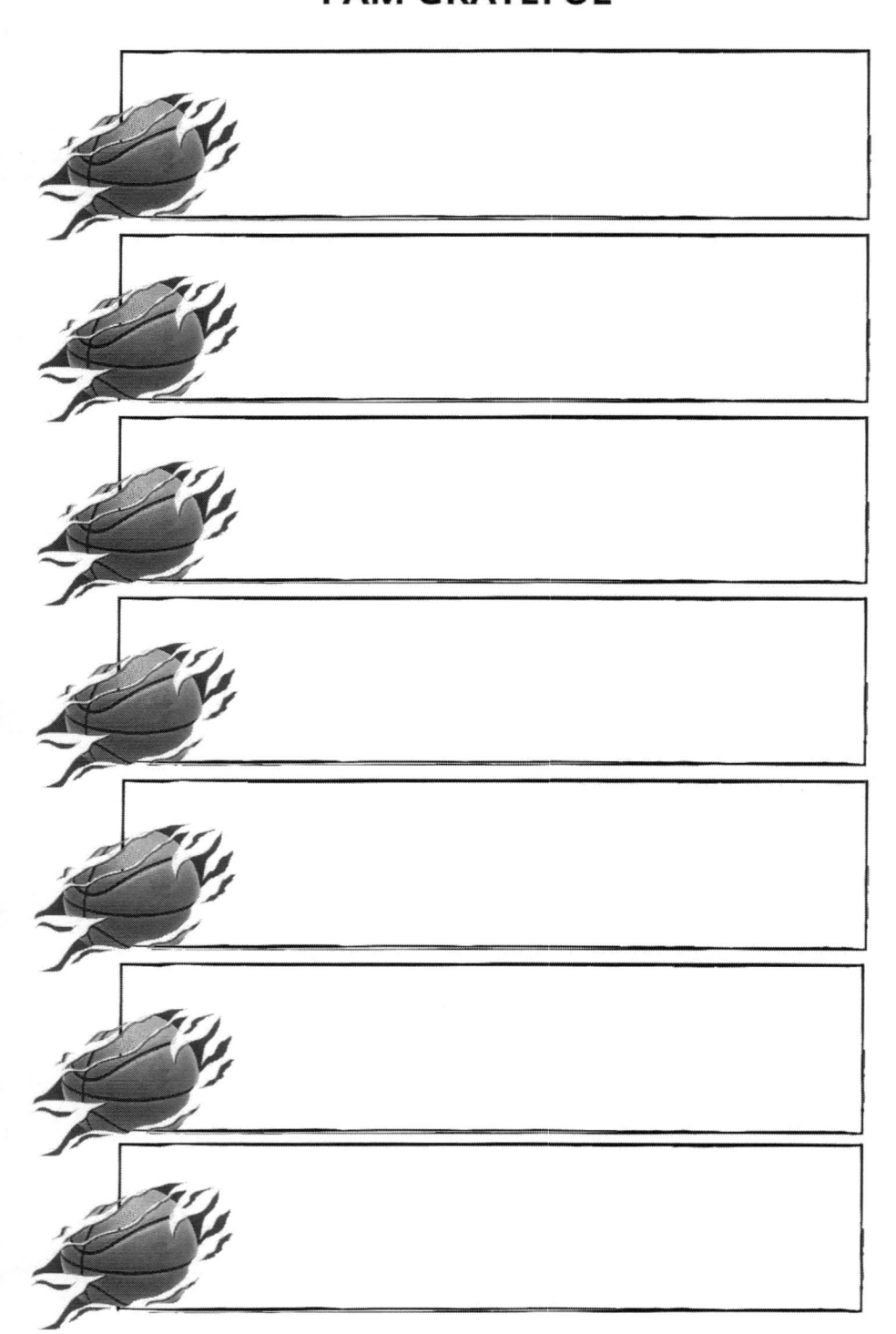

WEEK:_____   DATE:_____/_____/_____

I AM GRATEFUL

WEEK:_____   DATE:_____/_____/_____

THANK YOU

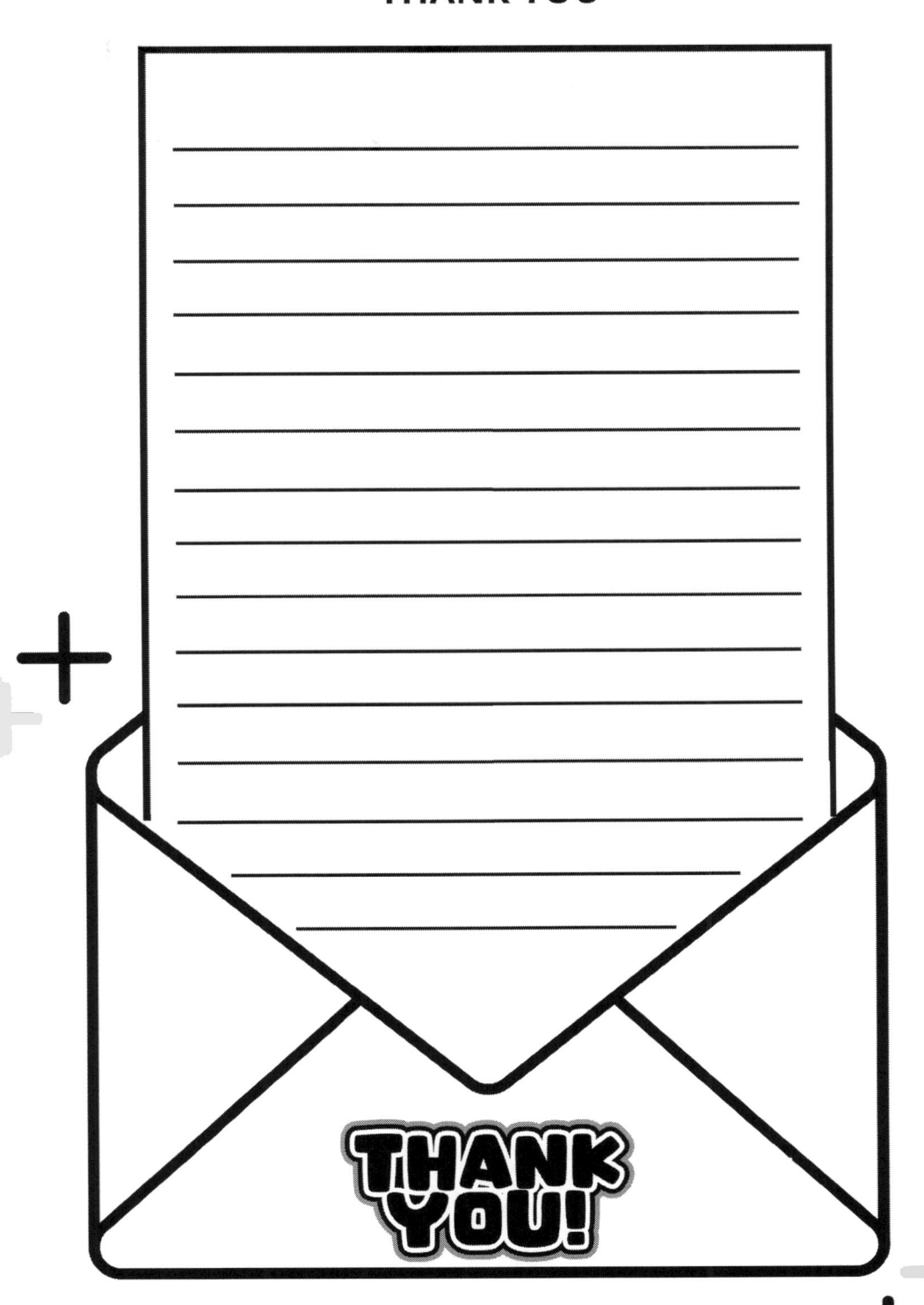

GOALS FOR THE MONTH

PERSONAL GOALS

TEAM GOALS

ACADEMIC GOALS

YOU MISS 100% OF THE SHOTS YOU never take

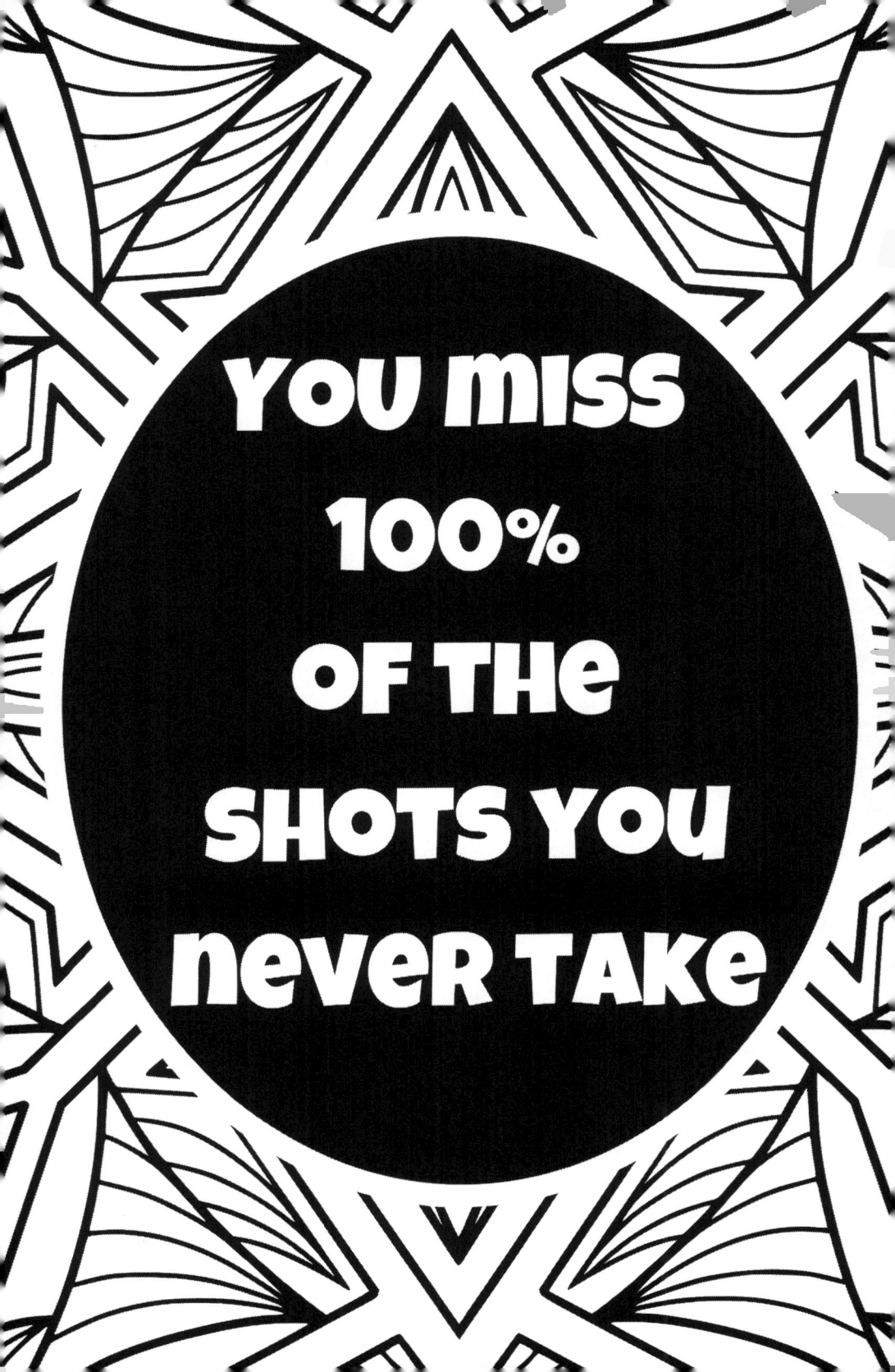

WEEK:_____   DATE:_____/_____/_____

HYDRATION

Week 1

Week 2

Week 3

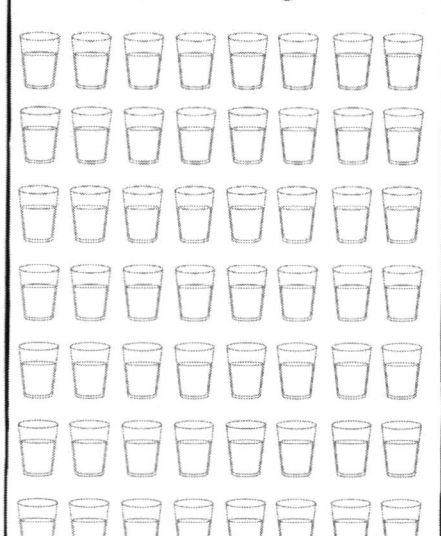

Week 4

WEEK:_____   DATE:_____/_____/_____

Show up every day and do the work.

ACCOMPLISHMENTS I'M PROUD OF
_____
_____
_____

HOW I HELPED MY TEAMMATES
_____
_____
_____

FAVORITE BASKETBALL MOMENTS
_____
_____
_____

GETTING BUCKETS - PRACTICE NOTES AND AT-HOME GOALS
_____
_____

SHOOTING _____ ☐

DRIBBLING _____ ☐

SPRINTS _____ ☐

DISTANCE RUN _____ ☐

WEEK:_____ DATE:_____/_____/_____

Who you are makes a difference.

ACCOMPLISHMENTS I'M PROUD OF
_____
_____
_____

HOW I HELPED MY TEAMMATES
_____
_____
_____

FAVORITE BASKETBALL MOMENTS
_____
_____
_____

GETTING BUCKETS - PRACTICE NOTES AND AT-HOME GOALS
_____
_____

SHOOTING _____ ☐
DRIBBLING _____ ☐
SPRINTS _____ ☐
DISTANCE RUN _____ ☐

WEEK:_____ DATE:_____/_____/_____

You matter!

ACCOMPLISHMENTS I'M PROUD OF
_____
_____
_____

HOW I HELPED MY TEAMMATES
_____
_____
_____
_____

FAVORITE BASKETBALL MOMENTS
_____
_____
_____
_____

GETTING BUCKETS - PRACTICE NOTES AND AT-HOME GOALS
_____
_____

SHOOTING _____ ☐

DRIBBLING _____ ☐

SPRINTS _____ ☐

DISTANCE RUN _____ ☐

WEEK:_____   DATE:_____/_____/_____

It's good to count to ten before you react.

ACCOMPLISHMENTS I'M PROUD OF
_____
_____
_____

HOW I HELPED MY TEAMMATES
_____
_____
_____
_____

FAVORITE BASKETBALL MOMENTS
_____
_____
_____
_____

GETTING BUCKETS - PRACTICE NOTES AND AT-HOME GOALS
_____
_____

SHOOTING _____ ☐

DRIBBLING _____ ☐

SPRINTS _____ ☐

DISTANCE RUN _____ ☐

WEEK:_____   DATE:_____/_____/_____

CELEBRATE MONTHLY PRACTICE WINS

Practice wins don't always have to be about learning new skills. Wins could be that you welcomed newcomers to your team and made them feel comfortable at a new club. Wins could be that you stayed positive even though you were having a hard day. Celebrating EVERY win is crucial to success and growth!

HOW DID MY SKILLS GROW?

_____
_____
_____
_____

HOW DID MY CHARACTER GROW?

_____
_____
_____
_____

HOW DID I GROW MENTALLY?

_____
_____
_____
_____

AFFIRMATIONS IN ACTION - visualize my goals as I say the statements below out loud.

When I did my _____, I felt _____
When my team _____, I felt _____

WEEK:_____   DATE:_____/_____/_____

MONTHLY REFLECTION

By knowing yourself you gain perspective and wisdom.

DID I REACH MY GOALS? If yes, what steps did I take to reach my goals? If not, what could I have done differently?

_____
_____
_____
_____

I WAS MOST POSITIVELY IMPACTED BY...

_____
_____
_____
_____

I POSITIVELY IMPACTED...

_____
_____
_____
_____

IN THE COMING WEEKS, I AM LOOKING FORWARD TO...

_____
_____
_____
_____

WEEK:_____   DATE:_____/_____/_____

VIDEO REVIEW NOTES

SUCCESSFUL MOMENTS WITHOUT THE BALL
_____
_____

SUCCESSFUL MOMENTS WITH THE BALL
_____
_____

MOMENTS I'D LIKE TO IMPROVE UPON
_____
_____

EFFORT LEVEL (1-5, 1 being the best effort)
Beginning _____ Middle _____ End _____

SUCCESSFUL MOMENTS WITHOUT THE BALL
_____
_____

SUCCESSFUL MOMENTS WITH THE BALL
_____
_____

MOMENTS I'D LIKE TO IMPROVE UPON
_____
_____

EFFORT LEVEL (1-5, 1 being the highest)
Beginning _____ Middle _____ End _____

WEEK:_____   DATE:_____/_____/_____

I AM GRATEFUL

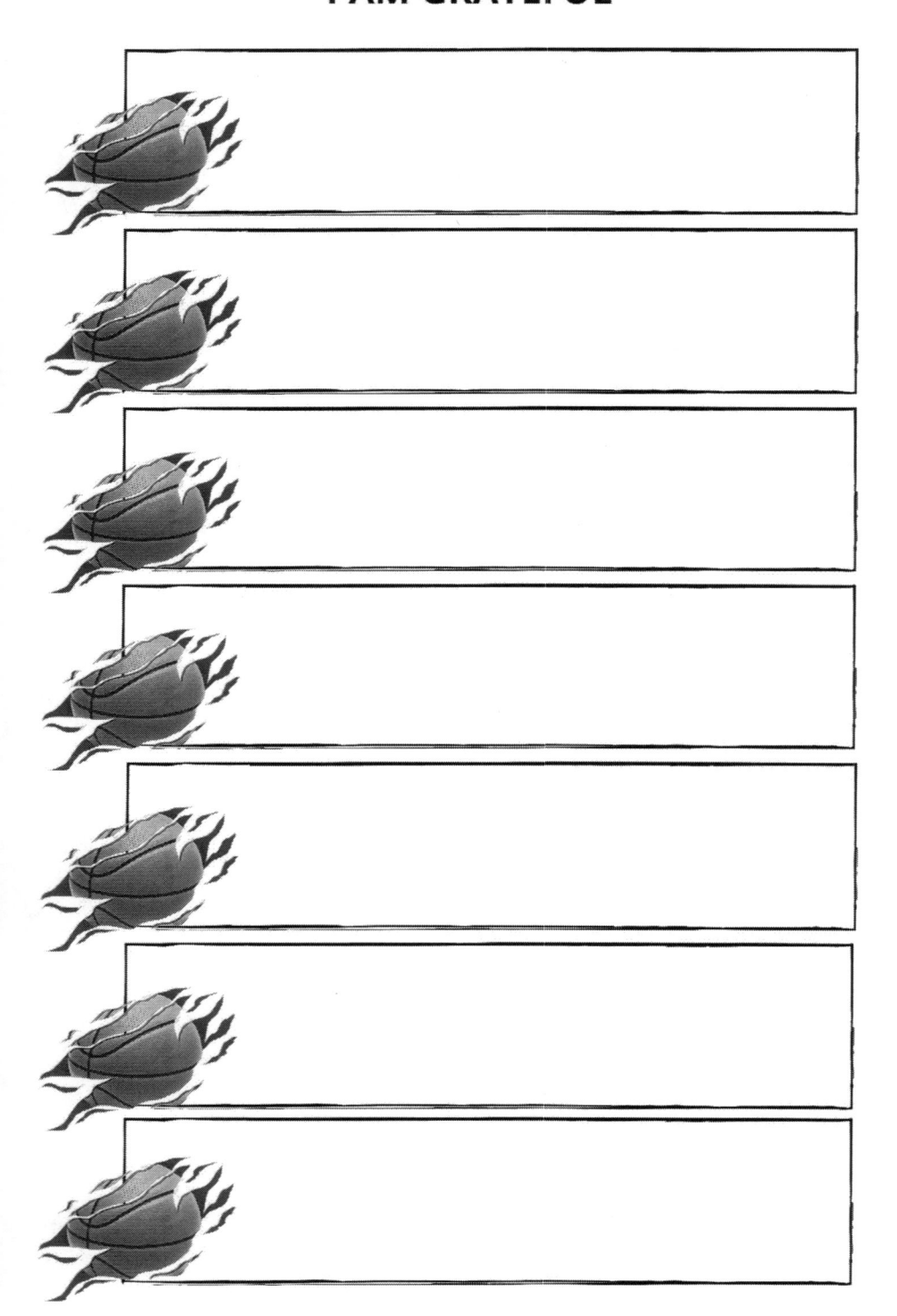

WEEK:_____   DATE:_____/_____/_____

THANK YOU

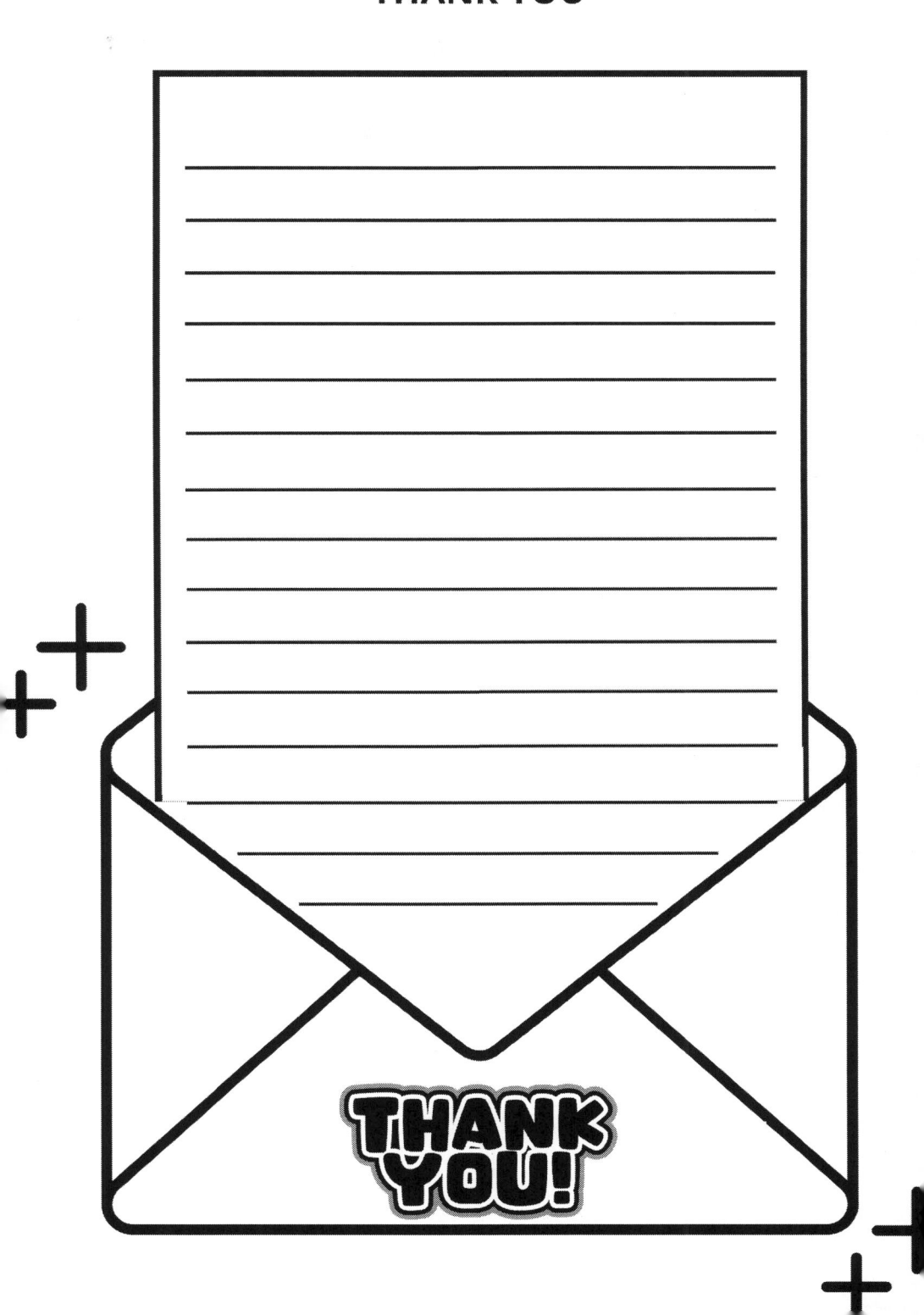

WEEK:_____   DATE:_____/_____/_____

GOALS FOR THE MONTH

PERSONAL GOALS

TEAM GOALS

ACADEMIC GOALS

WEEK:_____   DATE:_____/_____/_____

HYDRATION

Week 1

Week 2

Week 3

Week 4

WEEK:_____   DATE:_____/_____/_____

It's okay to get frustrated. Take a deep breath.

ACCOMPLISHMENTS I'M PROUD OF
_____
_____
_____

HOW I HELPED MY TEAMMATES
_____
_____
_____

FAVORITE BASKETBALL MOMENTS
_____
_____
_____

GETTING BUCKETS - PRACTICE NOTES AND AT-HOME GOALS
_____
_____

SHOOTING _____ ☐

DRIBBLING _____ ☐

SPRINTS _____ ☐

DISTANCE RUN _____ ☐

WEEK:_____   DATE:_____/_____/_____

Do something nice for someone else today.

ACCOMPLISHMENTS I'M PROUD OF
_____
_____
_____

HOW I HELPED MY TEAMMATES
_____
_____
_____

FAVORITE BASKETBALL MOMENTS
_____
_____
_____

GETTING BUCKETS - PRACTICE NOTES AND AT-HOME GOALS
_____
_____

SHOOTING _____ ☐
DRIBBLING _____ ☐
SPRINTS   _____ ☐
DISTANCE RUN _____ ☐

41

WEEK:_____ DATE:_____/_____/_____

Do your best to apply corrections.

ACCOMPLISHMENTS I'M PROUD OF

_____

_____

_____

HOW I HELPED MY TEAMMATES

_____

_____

_____

FAVORITE BASKETBALL MOMENTS

_____

_____

_____

GETTING BUCKETS - PRACTICE NOTES AND AT-HOME GOALS

_____

_____

SHOOTING _____ ☐

DRIBBLING _____ ☐

SPRINTS _____ ☐

DISTANCE RUN _____ ☐

WEEK:_____ DATE:____/____/____

Make sure you're drinking plenty of water.

ACCOMPLISHMENTS I'M PROUD OF

HOW I HELPED MY TEAMMATES

FAVORITE BASKETBALL MOMENTS

GETTING BUCKETS - PRACTICE NOTES AND AT-HOME GOALS

SHOOTING _____

DRIBBLING _____

SPRINTS _____

DISTANCE RUN _____

WEEK:_____   DATE:_____/_____/_____

Be sure to properly warm up and stretch your muscles.

ACCOMPLISHMENTS I'M PROUD OF
_____
_____
_____

HOW I HELPED MY TEAMMATES
_____
_____
_____

FAVORITE BASKETBALL MOMENTS
_____
_____
_____

GETTING BUCKETS - PRACTICE NOTES AND AT-HOME GOALS
_____
_____

SHOOTING _____ ☐

DRIBBLING _____ ☐

SPRINTS _____ ☐

DISTANCE RUN _____ ☐

WEEK:_____   DATE:_____/_____/_____

CELEBRATE MONTHLY PRACTICE WINS

Practice wins don't always have to be about learning new skills. Wins could be that you welcomed newcomers to your team and made them feel comfortable at a new club. Wins could be that you stayed positive even though you were having a hard day. Celebrating EVERY win is crucial to success and growth!

HOW DID MY SKILLS GROW?
_____
_____
_____
_____

HOW DID MY CHARACTER GROW?
_____
_____
_____
_____

HOW DID I GROW MENTALLY?
_____
_____
_____
_____

AFFIRMATIONS IN ACTION - visualize my goals as I say the statements below out loud.

When I did my _____, I felt _____
When my team _____, I felt_____

WEEK:_____   DATE:_____/_____/_____

MONTHLY REFLECTION

How we speak to others is a reflection of ourselves.

DID I REACH MY GOALS? If yes, what steps did I take to reach my goals? If not, what could I have done differently?

_____
_____
_____
_____

I WAS MOST POSITIVELY IMPACTED BY...

_____
_____
_____
_____

I POSITIVELY IMPACTED...

_____
_____
_____
_____

IN THE COMING WEEKS, I AM LOOKING FORWARD TO...

_____
_____
_____
_____

WEEK:_____   DATE:_____/_____/_____

VIDEO REVIEW NOTES

SUCCESSFUL MOMENTS WITHOUT THE BALL
_____
_____

SUCCESSFUL MOMENTS WITH THE BALL
_____
_____

MOMENTS I'D LIKE TO IMPROVE UPON
_____
_____

EFFORT LEVEL (1-5, 1 being the best effort)
Beginning _____ Middle _____End _____

SUCCESSFUL MOMENTS WITHOUT THE BALL
_____
_____

SUCCESSFUL MOMENTS WITH THE BALL
_____
_____

MOMENTS I'D LIKE TO IMPROVE UPON
_____
_____

EFFORT LEVEL (1-5, 1 being the highest)
Beginning _____ Middle _____End _____

WEEK:_____ DATE:_____/_____/_____

I AM GRATEFUL

WEEK:_____   DATE:_____/_____/_____

THANK YOU

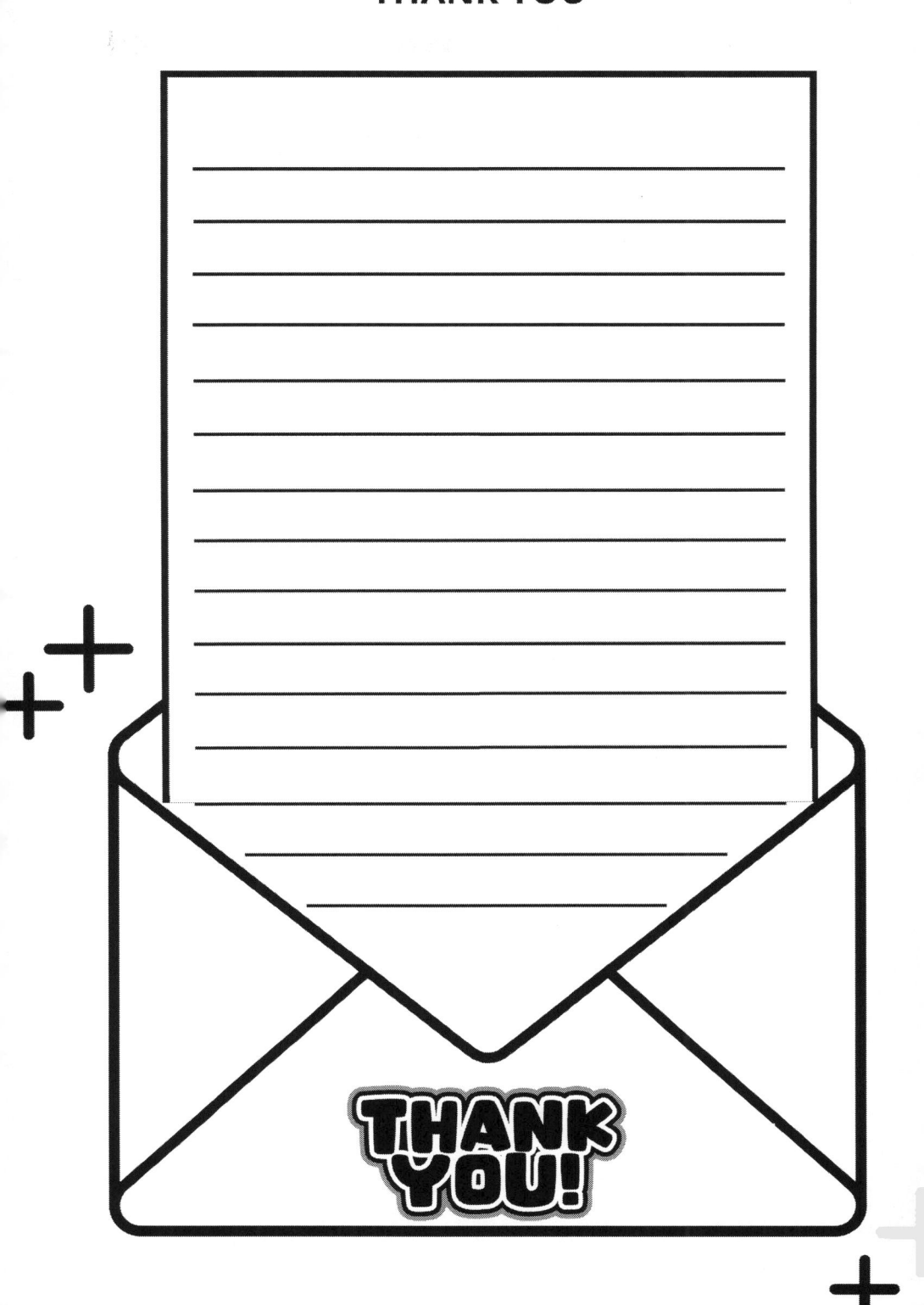

QUARTERLY BENCHMARK GOALS

PERSONAL GOALS

TEAM GOALS

ACADEMIC GOALS

PLAY HARD

DREAM BIG

WEEK:_____   DATE:_____/_____/_____

GOALS FOR THE MONTH

PERSONAL GOALS

TEAM GOALS

ACADEMIC GOALS

WEEK:_____   DATE:_____/_____/_____

HYDRATION

Week 1

Week 2

Week 3

Week 4

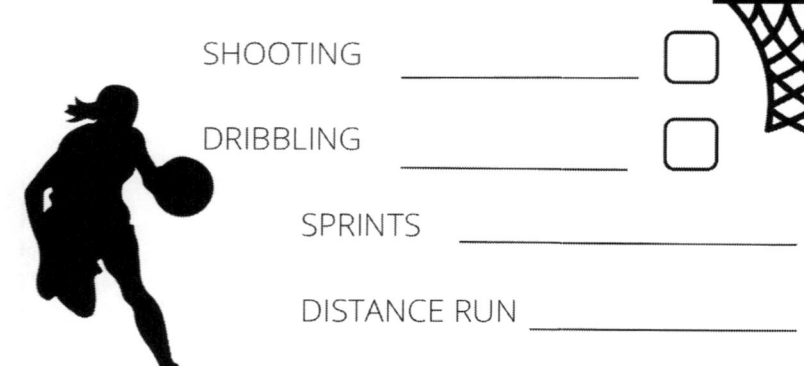

WEEK:_____   DATE:_____/_____/_____

Today is a new day, let go of past moments that bothered you.

ACCOMPLISHMENTS I'M PROUD OF
_____
_____
_____

HOW I HELPED MY TEAMMATES
_____
_____
_____

FAVORITE BASKETBALL MOMENTS
_____
_____
_____

GETTING BUCKETS - PRACTICE NOTES AND AT-HOME GOALS
_____
_____

SHOOTING _____ ☐

DRIBBLING _____ ☐

SPRINTS   _____ ☐

DISTANCE RUN _____ ☐

WEEK:_____   DATE:_____/_____/_____

Find a good book and read a chapter a day.

ACCOMPLISHMENTS I'M PROUD OF
_____
_____
_____

HOW I HELPED MY TEAMMATES
_____
_____
_____

FAVORITE BASKETBALL MOMENTS
_____
_____
_____

GETTING BUCKETS - PRACTICE NOTES AND AT-HOME GOALS
_____
_____

SHOOTING _____ ☐

DRIBBLING _____ ☐

SPRINTS _____ ☐

DISTANCE RUN _____ ☐

WEEK:_____   DATE:_____/_____/_____

LIVE - LOVE - BASKETBALL

ACCOMPLISHMENTS I'M PROUD OF
_____
_____
_____

HOW I HELPED MY TEAMMATES
_____
_____
_____

FAVORITE BASKETBALL MOMENTS
_____
_____
_____

GETTING BUCKETS - PRACTICE NOTES AND AT-HOME GOALS
_____
_____

SHOOTING _____ ☐

DRIBBLING _____ ☐

SPRINTS _____ ☐

DISTANCE RUN _____ ☐

WEEK:_____   DATE:_____/_____/_____

Doing your homework should be a priority.

ACCOMPLISHMENTS I'M PROUD OF
_____
_____
_____

HOW I HELPED MY TEAMMATES
_____
_____
_____

FAVORITE BASKETBALL MOMENTS
_____
_____
_____

GETTING BUCKETS - PRACTICE NOTES AND AT-HOME GOALS
_____
_____

SHOOTING _____ ☐

DRIBBLING _____ ☐

SPRINTS _____ ☐

DISTANCE RUN _____ ☐

WEEK:_____   DATE:_____/_____/_____

CELEBRATE MONTHLY PRACTICE WINS

Practice wins don't always have to be about learning new skills. Wins could be that you welcomed newcomers to your team and made them feel comfortable at a new club. Wins could be that you stayed positive even though you were having a hard day. Celebrating EVERY win is crucial to success and growth!

HOW DID MY SKILLS GROW?
_____
_____
_____
_____

HOW DID MY CHARACTER GROW?
_____
_____
_____
_____

HOW DID I GROW MENTALLY?
_____
_____
_____
_____

AFFIRMATIONS IN ACTION - visualize my goals as I say the statements below out loud.

When I did my _____, I felt _____
When my team _____, I felt _____

WEEK:_____   DATE:_____/_____/_____

MONTHLY REFLECTION

Gain insight into yourself through reflective thinking.

DID I REACH MY GOALS? If yes, what steps did I take to reach my goals? If not, what could I have done differently?

_____
_____
_____
_____

I WAS MOST POSITIVELY IMPACTED BY...

_____
_____
_____
_____

I POSITIVELY IMPACTED...

_____
_____
_____
_____

IN THE COMING WEEKS, I AM LOOKING FORWARD TO...

_____
_____
_____
_____

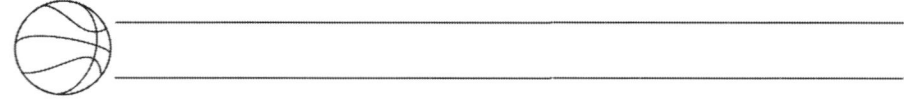

WEEK:_____   DATE:_____/_____/_____

VIDEO REVIEW NOTES

SUCCESSFUL MOMENTS WITHOUT THE BALL
_____
_____

SUCCESSFUL MOMENTS WITH THE BALL
_____
_____

MOMENTS I'D LIKE TO IMPROVE UPON
_____
_____

EFFORT LEVEL (1-5, 1 being the best effort)
Beginning _____ Middle _____ End _____

SUCCESSFUL MOMENTS WITHOUT THE BALL
_____
_____

SUCCESSFUL MOMENTS WITH THE BALL
_____
_____

MOMENTS I'D LIKE TO IMPROVE UPON
_____
_____

EFFORT LEVEL (1-5, 1 being the highest)
Beginning _____ Middle _____ End _____

WEEK:_____   DATE:_____/_____/_____

I AM GRATEFUL

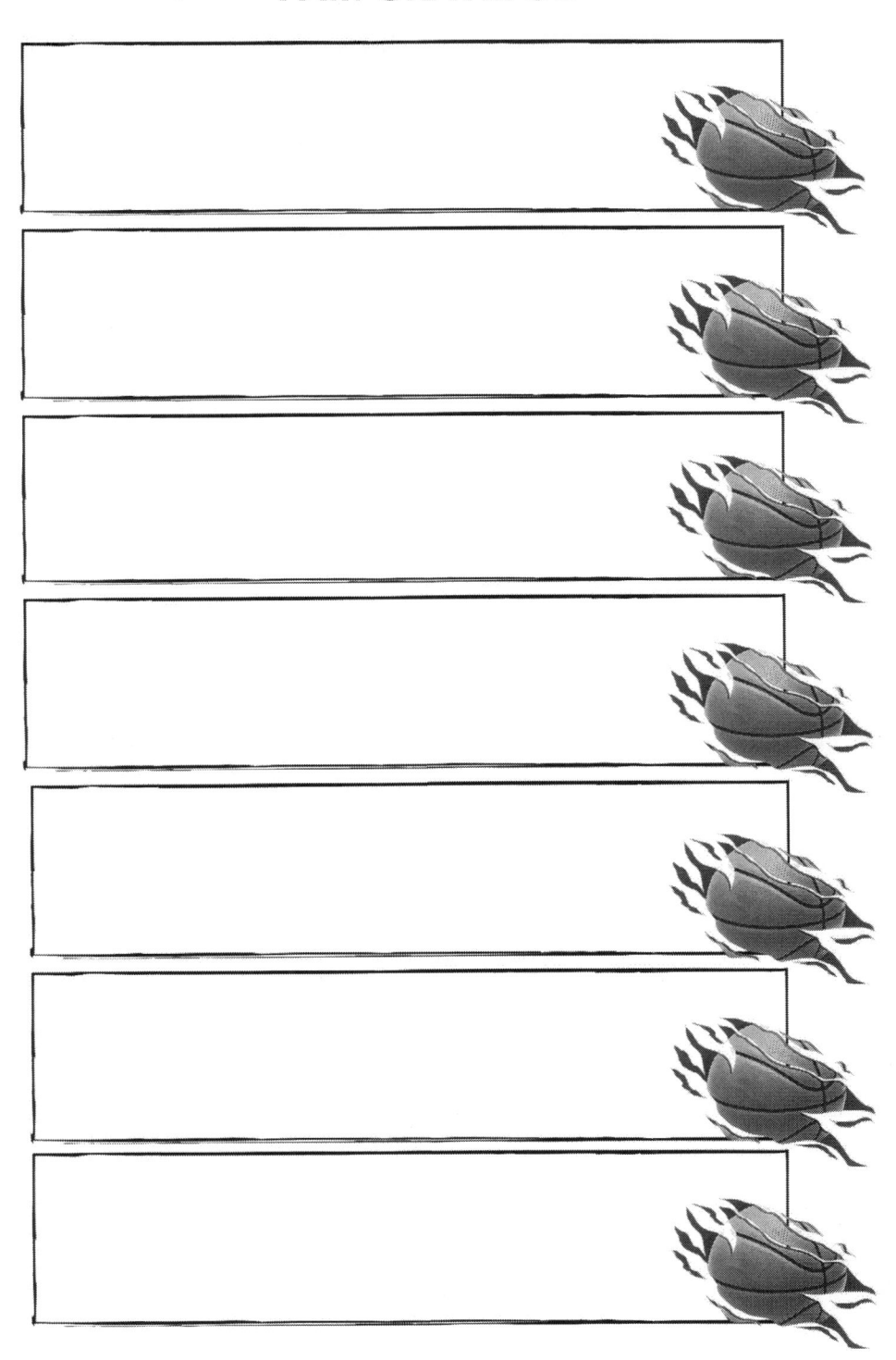

WEEK:_____   DATE:_____/_____/_____

THANK YOU

WEEK:_____   DATE:_____/_____/_____

GOALS FOR THE MONTH

PERSONAL GOALS

TEAM GOALS

ACADEMIC GOALS

WEEK:_____   DATE:_____/_____/_____
HYDRATION

Week 1

Week 2

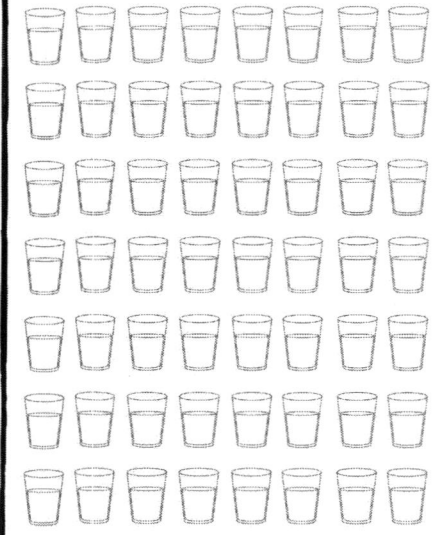

Week 3

Week 4

WEEK:_____ DATE:_____/_____/_____

Give your best effort at every practice.

ACCOMPLISHMENTS I'M PROUD OF
_____
_____
_____

HOW I HELPED MY TEAMMATES
_____
_____
_____

FAVORITE BASKETBALL MOMENTS
_____
_____
_____

GETTING BUCKETS - PRACTICE NOTES AND AT-HOME GOALS
_____
_____

SHOOTING _____ ☐
DRIBBLING _____ ☐
SPRINTS _____ ☐
DISTANCE RUN _____ ☐

WEEK:_____   DATE:_____/_____/_____

Your worth is not in the opinions of others.

ACCOMPLISHMENTS I'M PROUD OF
_____
_____
_____

HOW I HELPED MY TEAMMATES
_____
_____
_____

FAVORITE BASKETBALL MOMENTS
_____
_____
_____

GETTING BUCKETS - PRACTICE NOTES AND AT-HOME GOALS
_____
_____

SHOOTING _____ ☐

DRIBBLING _____ ☐

SPRINTS _____ ☐

DISTANCE RUN _____ ☐

WEEK:_____   DATE:_____/_____/_____

The world deserves who you were created to be.

ACCOMPLISHMENTS I'M PROUD OF
_____
_____
_____

HOW I HELPED MY TEAMMATES
_____
_____
_____

FAVORITE BASKETBALL MOMENTS
_____
_____
_____

GETTING BUCKETS - PRACTICE NOTES AND AT-HOME GOALS
_____
_____

SHOOTING _____ ☐

DRIBBLING _____ ☐

SPRINTS _____ ☐

DISTANCE RUN _____ ☐

WEEK:_____   DATE:_____/_____/_____

Your character is who you are on the inside.

ACCOMPLISHMENTS I'M PROUD OF
_____
_____
_____

HOW I HELPED MY TEAMMATES
_____
_____
_____

FAVORITE BASKETBALL MOMENTS
_____
_____
_____

GETTING BUCKETS - PRACTICE NOTES AND AT-HOME GOALS
_____
_____

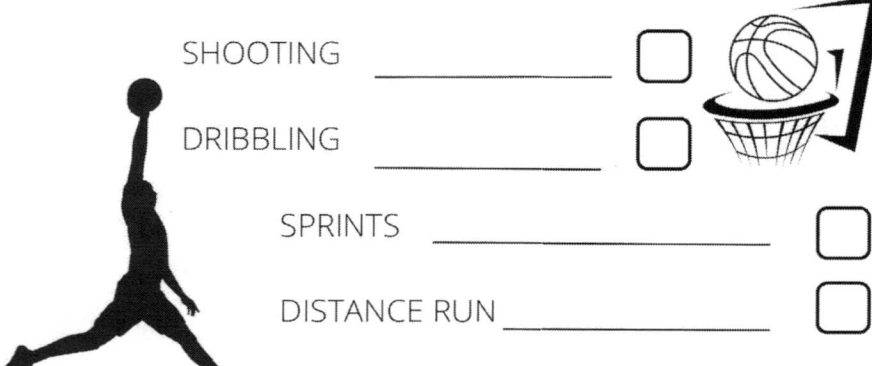

SHOOTING   _____ ☐
DRIBBLING   _____ ☐
SPRINTS   _____ ☐
DISTANCE RUN _____ ☐

WEEK:_____   DATE:_____/_____/_____

CELEBRATE MONTHLY PRACTICE WINS

Practice wins don't always have to be about learning new skills. Wins could be that you welcomed newcomers to your team and made them feel comfortable at a new club. Wins could be that you stayed positive even though you were having a hard day. Celebrating EVERY win is crucial to success and growth!

HOW DID MY SKILLS GROW?

_____
_____
_____
_____

HOW DID MY CHARACTER GROW?

_____
_____
_____
_____

HOW DID I GROW MENTALLY?

_____
_____
_____
_____

AFFIRMATIONS IN ACTION - visualize my goals as I say the statements below out loud.

When I did my _____, I felt _____
When my team _____, I felt _____

WEEK:_____ DATE:_____/_____/_____

MONTHLY REFLECTION

Remember that you cannot fail at being yourself.

DID I REACH MY GOALS? If yes, what steps did I take to reach my goals? If not, what could I have done differently?

_____
_____
_____
_____

I WAS MOST POSITIVELY IMPACTED BY...

_____
_____
_____
_____

I POSITIVELY IMPACTED...

_____
_____
_____
_____

IN THE COMING WEEKS, I AM LOOKING FORWARD TO...

_____
_____
_____
_____

WEEK:_____   DATE:_____/_____/_____

VIDEO REVIEW NOTES

SUCCESSFUL MOMENTS WITHOUT THE BALL
_____
_____

SUCCESSFUL MOMENTS WITH THE BALL
_____
_____

MOMENTS I'D LIKE TO IMPROVE UPON
_____
_____

EFFORT LEVEL (1-5, 1 being the best effort)
Beginning _____ Middle _____ End _____

SUCCESSFUL MOMENTS WITHOUT THE BALL
_____
_____

SUCCESSFUL MOMENTS WITH THE BALL
_____
_____

MOMENTS I'D LIKE TO IMPROVE UPON
_____
_____

EFFORT LEVEL (1-5, 1 being the highest)
Beginning _____ Middle _____ End _____

WEEK:_____   DATE:_____/_____/_____

I AM GRATEFUL

WEEK:_____   DATE:_____/_____/_____

THANK YOU

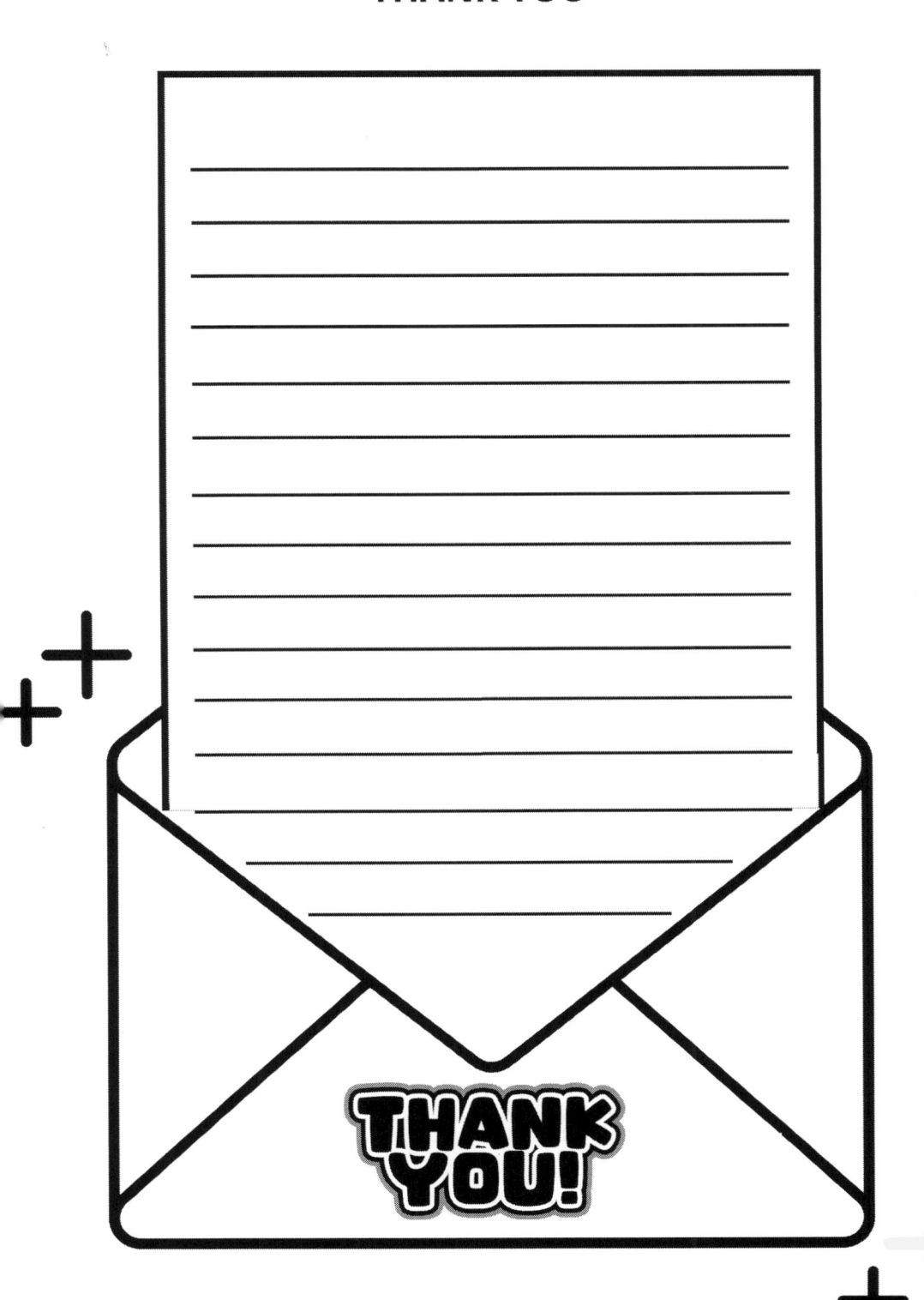

WEEK:_____   DATE:_____/_____/_____

GOALS FOR THE MONTH

PERSONAL GOALS

TEAM GOALS

ACADEMIC GOALS

WEEK:_____ DATE:_____/_____/_____

HYDRATION

Week 1

Week 2

Week 3

Week 4

WEEK:_____   DATE:_____/_____/_____

You can achieve anything you put your mind to.

ACCOMPLISHMENTS I'M PROUD OF
_____
_____
_____

HOW I HELPED MY TEAMMATES
_____
_____
_____

FAVORITE BASKETBALL MOMENTS
_____
_____
_____

GETTING BUCKETS - PRACTICE NOTES AND AT-HOME GOALS
_____
_____

SHOOTING _____ ☐

DRIBBLING _____ ☐

SPRINTS   _____ ☐

DISTANCE RUN _____ ☐

WEEK:_____   DATE:_____/_____/_____

When you get knocked down, get back up, and keep going.

ACCOMPLISHMENTS I'M PROUD OF
_____
_____
_____

HOW I HELPED MY TEAMMATES
_____
_____
_____

FAVORITE BASKETBALL MOMENTS
_____
_____
_____

GETTING BUCKETS - PRACTICE NOTES AND AT-HOME GOALS
_____
_____

SHOOTING _____ ☐
DRIBBLING _____ ☐
SPRINTS _____ ☐
DISTANCE RUN _____ ☐

WEEK:_____   DATE:_____/_____/_____

Dig deep, find out who you are and get to know yourself.

ACCOMPLISHMENTS I'M PROUD OF
_____
_____
_____

HOW I HELPED MY TEAMMATES
_____
_____
_____

FAVORITE BASKETBALL MOMENTS
_____
_____
_____

GETTING BUCKETS - PRACTICE NOTES AND AT-HOME GOALS
_____
_____

SHOOTING   _____ ☐
DRIBBLING   _____ ☐
SPRINTS   _____ ☐
DISTANCE RUN   _____ ☐

WEEK:_____   DATE:_____/_____/_____

Love yourself.

ACCOMPLISHMENTS I'M PROUD OF
_____
_____
_____

HOW I HELPED MY TEAMMATES
_____
_____
_____

FAVORITE BASKETBALL MOMENTS
_____
_____
_____

GETTING BUCKETS - PRACTICE NOTES AND AT-HOME GOALS
_____
_____

SHOOTING _____ ☐
DRIBBLING _____ ☐
SPRINTS _____ ☐
DISTANCE RUN _____ ☐

WEEK:_____   DATE:_____/_____/_____

Nothing easy is worth achieving. Do the work.

ACCOMPLISHMENTS I'M PROUD OF
_____
_____
_____

HOW I HELPED MY TEAMMATES
_____
_____
_____
_____

FAVORITE BASKETBALL MOMENTS
_____
_____
_____
_____

GETTING BUCKETS - PRACTICE NOTES AND AT-HOME GOALS
_____
_____

SHOOTING _____ ☐

DRIBBLING _____ ☐

SPRINTS _____ ☐

DISTANCE RUN _____ ☐

WEEK:_____   DATE:_____/_____/_____

CELEBRATE MONTHLY PRACTICE WINS

Practice wins don't always have to be about learning new skills. Wins could be that you welcomed newcomers to your team and made them feel comfortable at a new club. Wins could be that you stayed positive even though you were having a hard day. Celebrating EVERY win is crucial to success and growth!

HOW DID MY SKILLS GROW?
_____
_____
_____
_____

HOW DID MY CHARACTER GROW?
_____
_____
_____
_____

HOW DID I GROW MENTALLY?
_____
_____
_____
_____

AFFIRMATIONS IN ACTION - visualize my goals as I say the statements below out loud.

When I did my _____, I felt _____
When my team _____, I felt _____

WEEK:_____   DATE:_____/_____/_____

MONTHLY REFLECTION

Everyone has faults. Know your faults and own them.

DID I REACH MY GOALS? If yes, what steps did I take to reach my goals? If not, what could I have done differently?

_____
_____
_____
_____

I WAS MOST POSITIVELY IMPACTED BY...

_____
_____
_____
_____

I POSITIVELY IMPACTED...

_____
_____
_____
_____

IN THE COMING WEEKS, I AM LOOKING FORWARD TO...

_____
_____
_____
_____

WEEK:_____   DATE:_____/_____/_____

VIDEO REVIEW NOTES

SUCCESSFUL MOMENTS WITHOUT THE BALL
_____
_____

SUCCESSFUL MOMENTS WITH THE BALL
_____
_____

MOMENTS I'D LIKE TO IMPROVE UPON
_____
_____

EFFORT LEVEL (1-5, 1 being the best effort)
Beginning _____ Middle _____ End _____

SUCCESSFUL MOMENTS WITHOUT THE BALL
_____
_____

SUCCESSFUL MOMENTS WITH THE BALL
_____
_____

MOMENTS I'D LIKE TO IMPROVE UPON
_____
_____

EFFORT LEVEL (1-5, 1 being the highest)
Beginning _____ Middle _____ End _____

WEEK:_____ DATE:_____/_____/_____

I AM GRATEFUL

WEEK:_____ DATE:_____/_____/_____

THANK YOU

QUARTERLY BENCHMARK GOALS

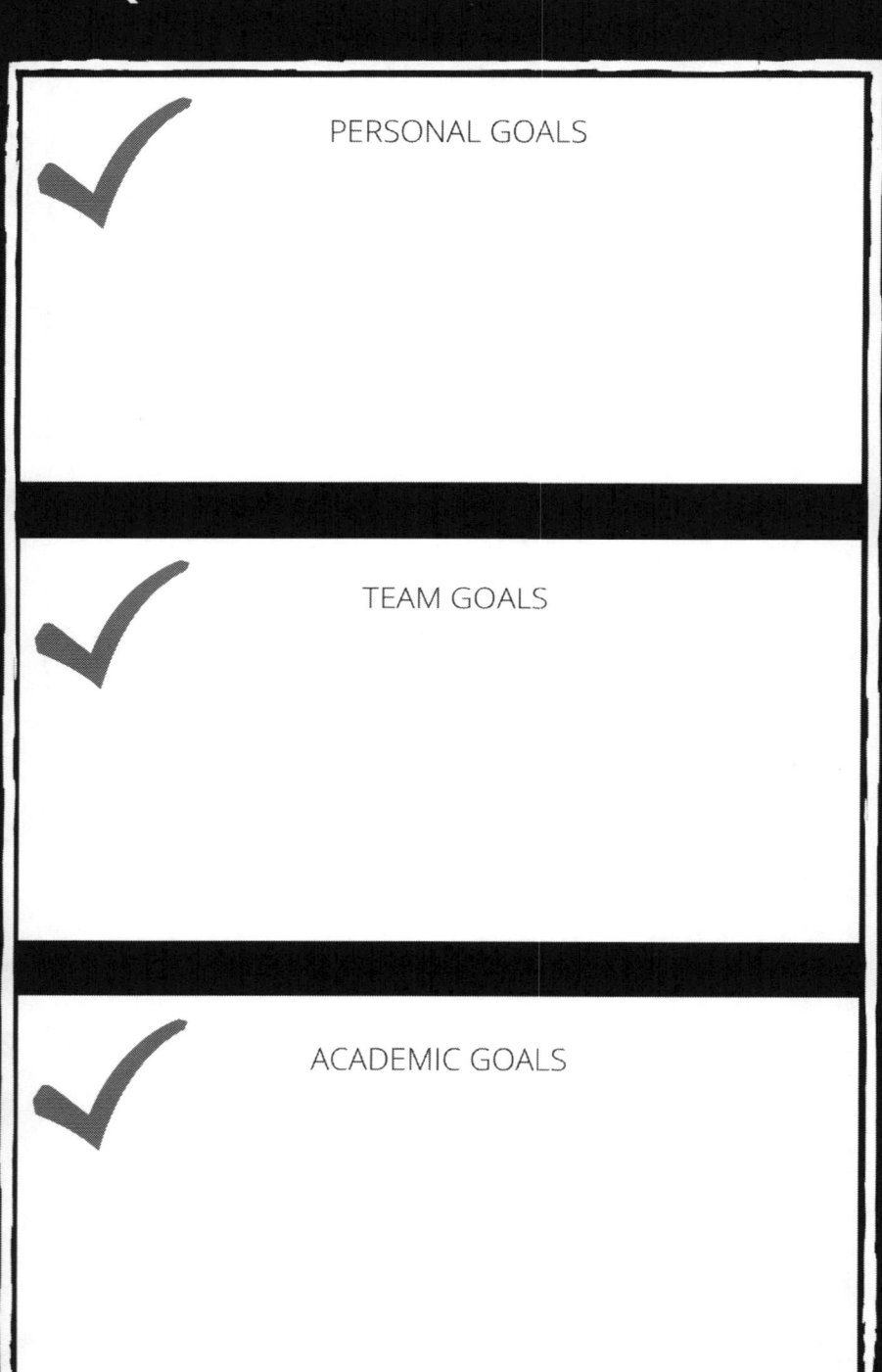

✓ PERSONAL GOALS

✓ TEAM GOALS

✓ ACADEMIC GOALS

"YOU CAN'T WIN UNLESS YOU LEARN HOW TO LOSE"

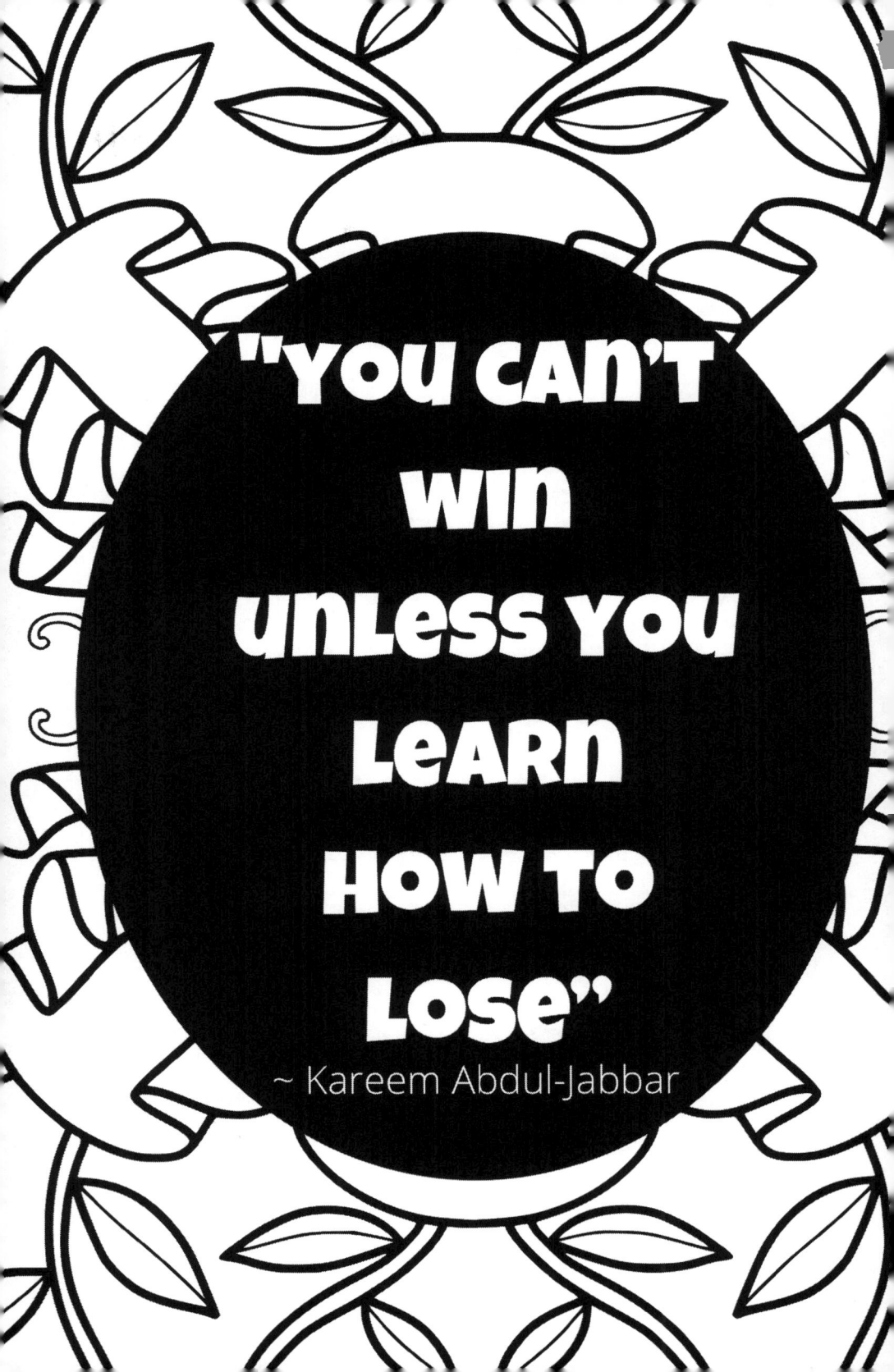

~ Kareem Abdul-Jabbar

WEEK:_____ DATE:_____/_____/_____

GOALS FOR THE MONTH

PERSONAL GOALS

TEAM GOALS

ACADEMIC GOALS

WEEK:_____   DATE:_____/_____/_____

HYDRATION

Week 1

Week 2

Week 3

Week 4

WEEK:_____   DATE:_____/_____/_____

Be humble. Arrogance is unbecoming.

ACCOMPLISHMENTS I'M PROUD OF
_____
_____
_____

HOW I HELPED MY TEAMMATES
_____
_____
_____

FAVORITE BASKETBALL MOMENTS
_____
_____
_____

GETTING BUCKETS - PRACTICE NOTES AND AT-HOME GOALS
_____
_____

SHOOTING _____ ☐

DRIBBLING _____ ☐

SPRINTS _____ ☐

DISTANCE RUN _____ ☐

WEEK:_____ DATE:_____/_____/_____

Be genuine in your thoughts, actions, and feelings.

ACCOMPLISHMENTS I'M PROUD OF
_____
_____
_____

HOW I HELPED MY TEAMMATES
_____
_____
_____

FAVORITE BASKETBALL MOMENTS
_____
_____
_____

GETTING BUCKETS - PRACTICE NOTES AND AT-HOME GOALS
_____
_____

SHOOTING _____ ☐
DRIBBLING _____ ☐
SPRINTS _____ ☐
DISTANCE RUN _____ ☐

WEEK:_____   DATE:_____/_____/_____

You rise by lifting others.

ACCOMPLISHMENTS I'M PROUD OF
_____
_____
_____

HOW I HELPED MY TEAMMATES
_____
_____
_____

FAVORITE BASKETBALL MOMENTS
_____
_____
_____

GETTING BUCKETS - PRACTICE NOTES AND AT-HOME GOALS
_____
_____

SHOOTING _____ ☐

DRIBBLING _____ ☐

SPRINTS _____ ☐

DISTANCE RUN _____ ☐

WEEK:_____   DATE:_____/_____/_____

You can't buy happiness. You must find it within.

ACCOMPLISHMENTS I'M PROUD OF
_____
_____
_____

HOW I HELPED MY TEAMMATES
_____
_____
_____

FAVORITE BASKETBALL MOMENTS
_____
_____
_____

GETTING BUCKETS - PRACTICE NOTES AND AT-HOME GOALS
_____
_____

SHOOTING _____ ☐
DRIBBLING _____ ☐
SPRINTS _____ ☐
DISTANCE RUN _____ ☐

WEEK:_____ DATE:_____/_____/_____

CELEBRATE MONTHLY PRACTICE WINS

Practice wins don't always have to be about learning new skills. Wins could be that you welcomed newcomers to your team and made them feel comfortable at a new club. Wins could be that you stayed positive even though you were having a hard day. Celebrating EVERY win is crucial to success and growth!

HOW DID MY SKILLS GROW?

_____
_____
_____
_____

HOW DID MY CHARACTER GROW?

_____
_____
_____
_____

HOW DID I GROW MENTALLY?

_____
_____
_____
_____

AFFIRMATIONS IN ACTION - visualize my goals as I say the statements below out loud.

When I did my _____, I felt _____
When my team _____, I felt _____

WEEK:_____ DATE:_____/_____/_____

MONTHLY REFLECTION

Reflecting on the past can be the key to the future.

DID I REACH MY GOALS? If yes, what steps did I take to reach my goals? If not, what could I have done differently?

_____
_____
_____
_____

I WAS MOST POSITIVELY IMPACTED BY...

_____
_____
_____
_____

I POSITIVELY IMPACTED...

_____
_____
_____
_____

IN THE COMING WEEKS, I AM LOOKING FORWARD TO...

_____
_____
_____
_____

WEEK:_____   DATE:_____/_____/_____

VIDEO REVIEW NOTES

SUCCESSFUL MOMENTS WITHOUT THE BALL
_____
_____

SUCCESSFUL MOMENTS WITH THE BALL
_____
_____

MOMENTS I'D LIKE TO IMPROVE UPON
_____
_____

EFFORT LEVEL (1-5, 1 being the best effort)
Beginning _____ Middle _____ End _____

SUCCESSFUL MOMENTS WITHOUT THE BALL
_____
_____

SUCCESSFUL MOMENTS WITH THE BALL
_____
_____

MOMENTS I'D LIKE TO IMPROVE UPON
_____
_____

EFFORT LEVEL (1-5, 1 being the highest)
Beginning _____ Middle _____ End _____

WEEK:_____   DATE:_____/_____/_____

I AM GRATEFUL

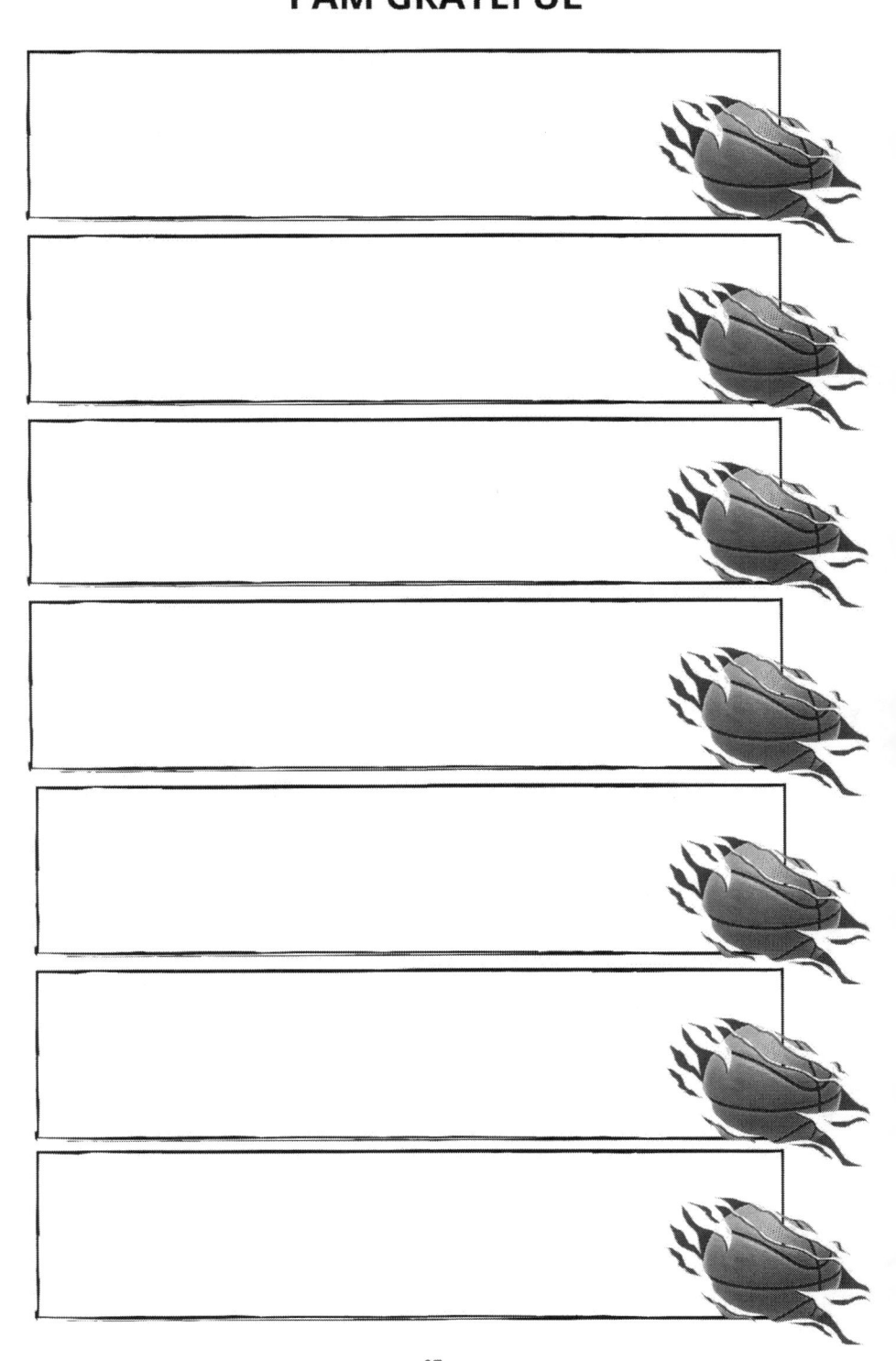

WEEK:_____   DATE:_____/_____/_____

THANK YOU

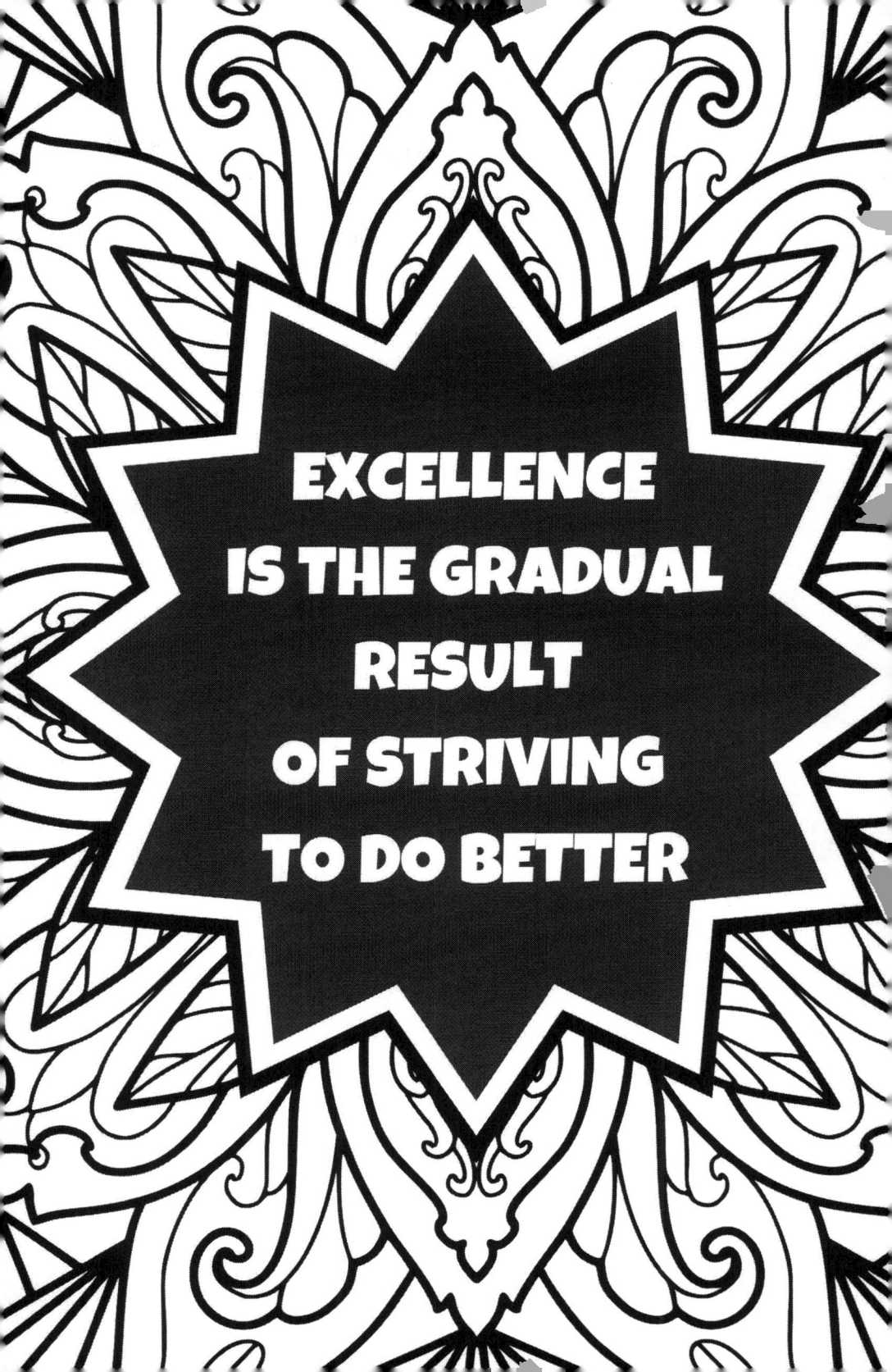

EXCELLENCE IS THE GRADUAL RESULT OF STRIVING TO DO BETTER

WEEK:_____   DATE:_____/_____/_____

GOALS FOR THE MONTH

PERSONAL GOALS

TEAM GOALS

ACADEMIC GOALS

WEEK:_____   DATE:_____/_____/_____

HYDRATION

Week 1

Week 2

Week 3

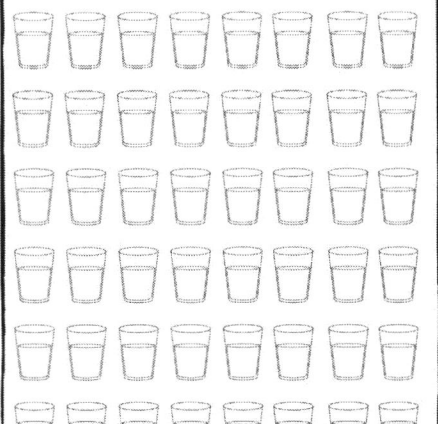

Week 4

WEEK:_____ DATE:_____/_____/_____

> If at first, you don't succeed. Keep working, success is near.

ACCOMPLISHMENTS I'M PROUD OF

HOW I HELPED MY TEAMMATES

FAVORITE BASKETBALL MOMENTS

GETTING BUCKETS - PRACTICE NOTES AND AT-HOME GOALS

SHOOTING _____ ☐

DRIBBLING _____ ☐

SPRINTS _____ ☐

DISTANCE RUN _____ ☐

WEEK:_____   DATE:_____/_____/_____

Things don't always go your way. Keep going anyway.

ACCOMPLISHMENTS I'M PROUD OF
_____
_____
_____

HOW I HELPED MY TEAMMATES
_____
_____
_____

FAVORITE BASKETBALL MOMENTS
_____
_____
_____

GETTING BUCKETS - PRACTICE NOTES AND AT-HOME GOALS
_____
_____

SHOOTING _____ ☐
DRIBBLING _____ ☐
SPRINTS _____ ☐
DISTANCE RUN _____ ☐

WEEK:_____   DATE:_____/_____/_____

People aren't always kind. Be kind anyway.

ACCOMPLISHMENTS I'M PROUD OF
_____
_____
_____

HOW I HELPED MY TEAMMATES
_____
_____
_____

FAVORITE BASKETBALL MOMENTS
_____
_____
_____

GETTING BUCKETS - PRACTICE NOTES AND AT-HOME GOALS
_____
_____

SHOOTING _____ ☐
DRIBBLING _____ ☐
SPRINTS _____ ☐
DISTANCE RUN _____ ☐

WEEK:_____   DATE:_____/_____/_____

Every day is what you make it, so make it great.

ACCOMPLISHMENTS I'M PROUD OF
_____
_____
_____

HOW I HELPED MY TEAMMATES
_____
_____
_____

FAVORITE BASKETBALL MOMENTS
_____
_____
_____

GETTING BUCKETS - PRACTICE NOTES AND AT-HOME GOALS
_____
_____

SHOOTING _____ ☐

DRIBBLING _____ ☐

SPRINTS _____ ☐

DISTANCE RUN _____ ☐

WEEK:_____   DATE:_____/_____/_____

CELEBRATE MONTHLY PRACTICE WINS

Practice wins don't always have to be about learning new skills. Wins could be that you welcomed newcomers to your team and made them feel comfortable at a new club. Wins could be that you stayed positive even though you were having a hard day. Celebrating EVERY win is crucial to success and growth!

HOW DID MY SKILLS GROW?
_____
_____
_____
_____

HOW DID MY CHARACTER GROW?
_____
_____
_____
_____

HOW DID I GROW MENTALLY?
_____
_____
_____
_____

AFFIRMATIONS IN ACTION - visualize my goals as I say the statements below out loud.

When I did my _____, I felt _____
When my team _____, I felt _____

WEEK:_____   DATE:_____/_____/_____

MONTHLY REFLECTION

Self reflection brings awareness.

DID I REACH MY GOALS? If yes, what steps did I take to reach my goals? If not, what could I have done differently?

_____
_____
_____
_____

I WAS MOST POSITIVELY IMPACTED BY...

_____
_____
_____
_____

I POSITIVELY IMPACTED...

_____
_____
_____
_____

IN THE COMING WEEKS, I AM LOOKING FORWARD TO...

_____
_____
_____
_____

WEEK:_____   DATE:_____/_____/_____

VIDEO REVIEW NOTES

SUCCESSFUL MOMENTS WITHOUT THE BALL
_____
_____

SUCCESSFUL MOMENTS WITH THE BALL
_____
_____

MOMENTS I'D LIKE TO IMPROVE UPON
_____
_____

EFFORT LEVEL (1-5, 1 being the best effort)
Beginning _____ Middle _____ End _____

SUCCESSFUL MOMENTS WITHOUT THE BALL
_____
_____

SUCCESSFUL MOMENTS WITH THE BALL
_____
_____

MOMENTS I'D LIKE TO IMPROVE UPON
_____
_____

EFFORT LEVEL (1-5, 1 being the highest)
Beginning _____ Middle _____ End _____

WEEK:_____   DATE:_____/_____/_____

I AM GRATEFUL

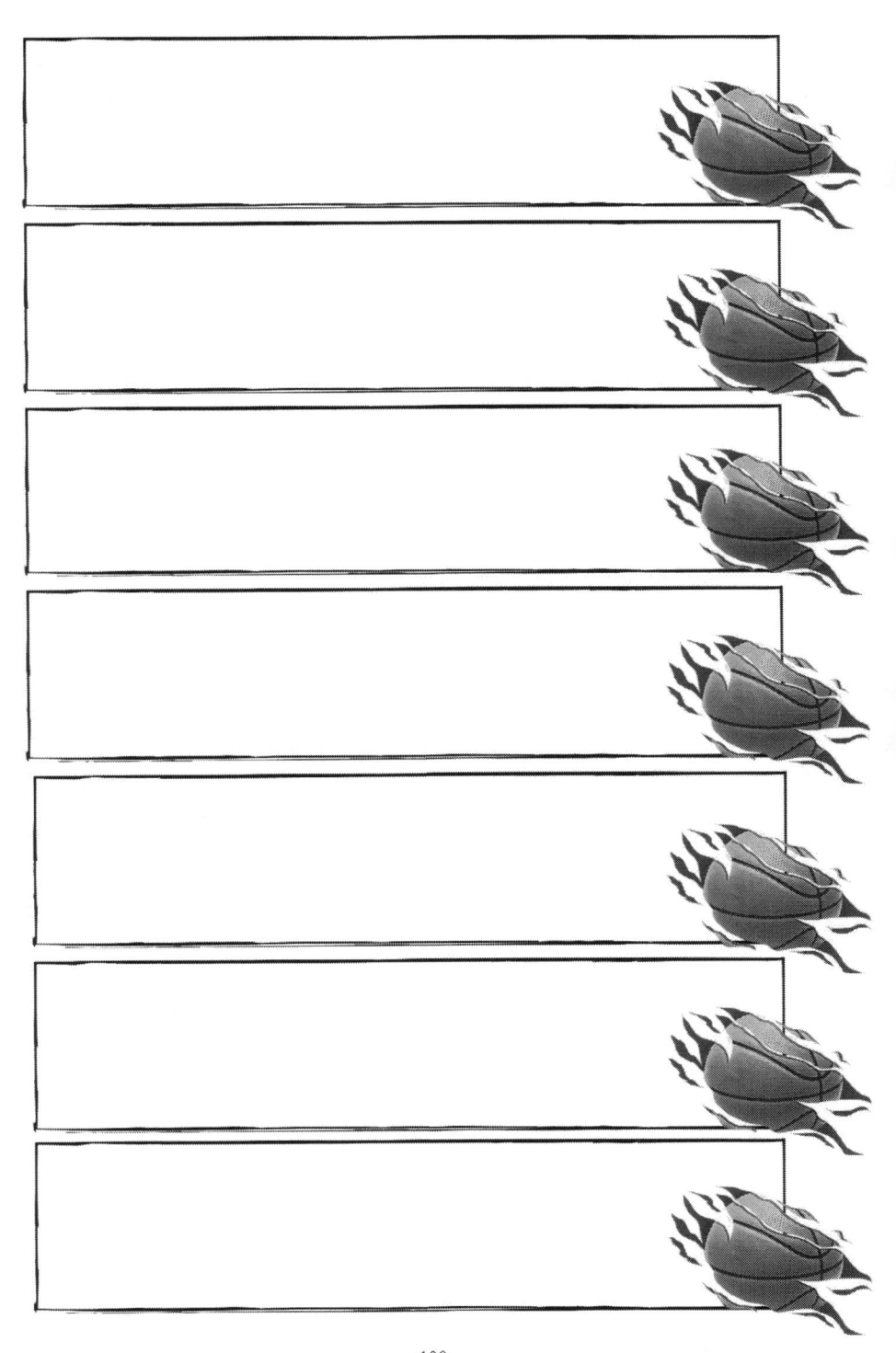

WEEK:_____   DATE:_____/_____/_____

THANK YOU

WEEK:_____ DATE:_____/_____/_____

GOALS FOR THE MONTH

PERSONAL GOALS

TEAM GOALS

ACADEMIC GOALS

WEEK:_____   DATE:_____/_____/_____

HYDRATION

Week 1

Week 2

Week 3

Week 4

WEEK:_____   DATE:_____ / _____ / _____

Celebrate others accomplishments.

ACCOMPLISHMENTS I'M PROUD OF
_____
_____
_____

HOW I HELPED MY TEAMMATES
_____
_____
_____

FAVORITE BASKETBALL MOMENTS
_____
_____
_____

GETTING BUCKETS - PRACTICE NOTES AND AT-HOME GOALS
_____
_____

SHOOTING _____ ☐

DRIBBLING _____ ☐

SPRINTS _____ ☐

DISTANCE RUN _____ ☐

WEEK:_____   DATE:_____/_____/_____

A bad day is a fleeting moment in time, tomorrow is a new day.

ACCOMPLISHMENTS I'M PROUD OF
_____
_____
_____

HOW I HELPED MY TEAMMATES
_____
_____
_____

FAVORITE BASKETBALL MOMENTS
_____
_____
_____

GETTING BUCKETS - PRACTICE NOTES AND AT-HOME GOALS
_____

SHOOTING _____ ☐

DRIBBLING _____ ☐

SPRINTS   _____ ☐

DISTANCE RUN _____ ☐

WEEK:_____   DATE:_____/_____/_____

Believe and you will achieve.

ACCOMPLISHMENTS I'M PROUD OF
_____
_____
_____

HOW I HELPED MY TEAMMATES
_____
_____
_____

FAVORITE BASKETBALL MOMENTS
_____
_____
_____

GETTING BUCKETS - PRACTICE NOTES AND AT-HOME GOALS
_____
_____

SHOOTING _____ ☐
DRIBBLING _____ ☐
SPRINTS _____ ☐
DISTANCE RUN _____ ☐

WEEK:_____   DATE:_____/_____/_____

Remember what you love most about basketball.

ACCOMPLISHMENTS I'M PROUD OF
_____
_____
_____

HOW I HELPED MY TEAMMATES
_____
_____
_____

FAVORITE BASKETBALL MOMENTS
_____
_____
_____

GETTING BUCKETS - PRACTICE NOTES AND AT-HOME GOALS
_____
_____

SHOOTING _____ ☐

DRIBBLING _____ ☐

SPRINTS _____ ☐

DISTANCE RUN _____ ☐

WEEK:_____ DATE:_____/_____/_____

Your success is completely up to you.

ACCOMPLISHMENTS I'M PROUD OF
_____
_____
_____

HOW I HELPED MY TEAMMATES
_____
_____
_____

FAVORITE BASKETBALL MOMENTS
_____
_____
_____

GETTING BUCKETS - PRACTICE NOTES AND AT-HOME GOALS
_____
_____

SHOOTING _____ ☐
DRIBBLING _____ ☐
SPRINTS _____ ☐
DISTANCE RUN _____ ☐

WEEK:_____   DATE:_____/_____/_____

CELEBRATE MONTHLY PRACTICE WINS

Practice wins don't always have to be about learning new skills. Wins could be that you welcomed newcomers to your team and made them feel comfortable at a new club. Wins could be that you stayed positive even though you were having a hard day. Celebrating EVERY win is crucial to success and growth!

HOW DID MY SKILLS GROW?

_____
_____
_____
_____

HOW DID MY CHARACTER GROW?

_____
_____
_____
_____

HOW DID I GROW MENTALLY?

_____
_____
_____
_____

AFFIRMATIONS IN ACTION - visualize my goals as I say the statements below out loud.

When I did my _____, I felt _____
When my team _____, I felt _____

WEEK:_____ DATE:_____/_____/_____

MONTHLY REFLECTION

The more you reflect the more you learn about yourself.

DID I REACH MY GOALS? If yes, what steps did I take to reach my goals? If not, what could I have done differently?

_____
_____
_____
_____

I WAS MOST POSITIVELY IMPACTED BY...

_____
_____
_____
_____

I POSITIVELY IMPACTED...

_____
_____
_____
_____

IN THE COMING WEEKS, I AM LOOKING FORWARD TO...

_____
_____
_____
_____

WEEK:_____   DATE:_____/_____/_____

VIDEO REVIEW NOTES

SUCCESSFUL MOMENTS WITHOUT THE BALL
_____
_____

SUCCESSFUL MOMENTS WITH THE BALL
_____
_____

MOMENTS I'D LIKE TO IMPROVE UPON
_____
_____

EFFORT LEVEL (1-5, 1 being the best effort)
Beginning _____ Middle _____ End _____

SUCCESSFUL MOMENTS WITHOUT THE BALL
_____
_____

SUCCESSFUL MOMENTS WITH THE BALL
_____
_____

MOMENTS I'D LIKE TO IMPROVE UPON
_____
_____

EFFORT LEVEL (1-5, 1 being the highest)
Beginning _____ Middle _____ End _____

WEEK:_____   DATE:_____/_____/_____

I AM GRATEFUL

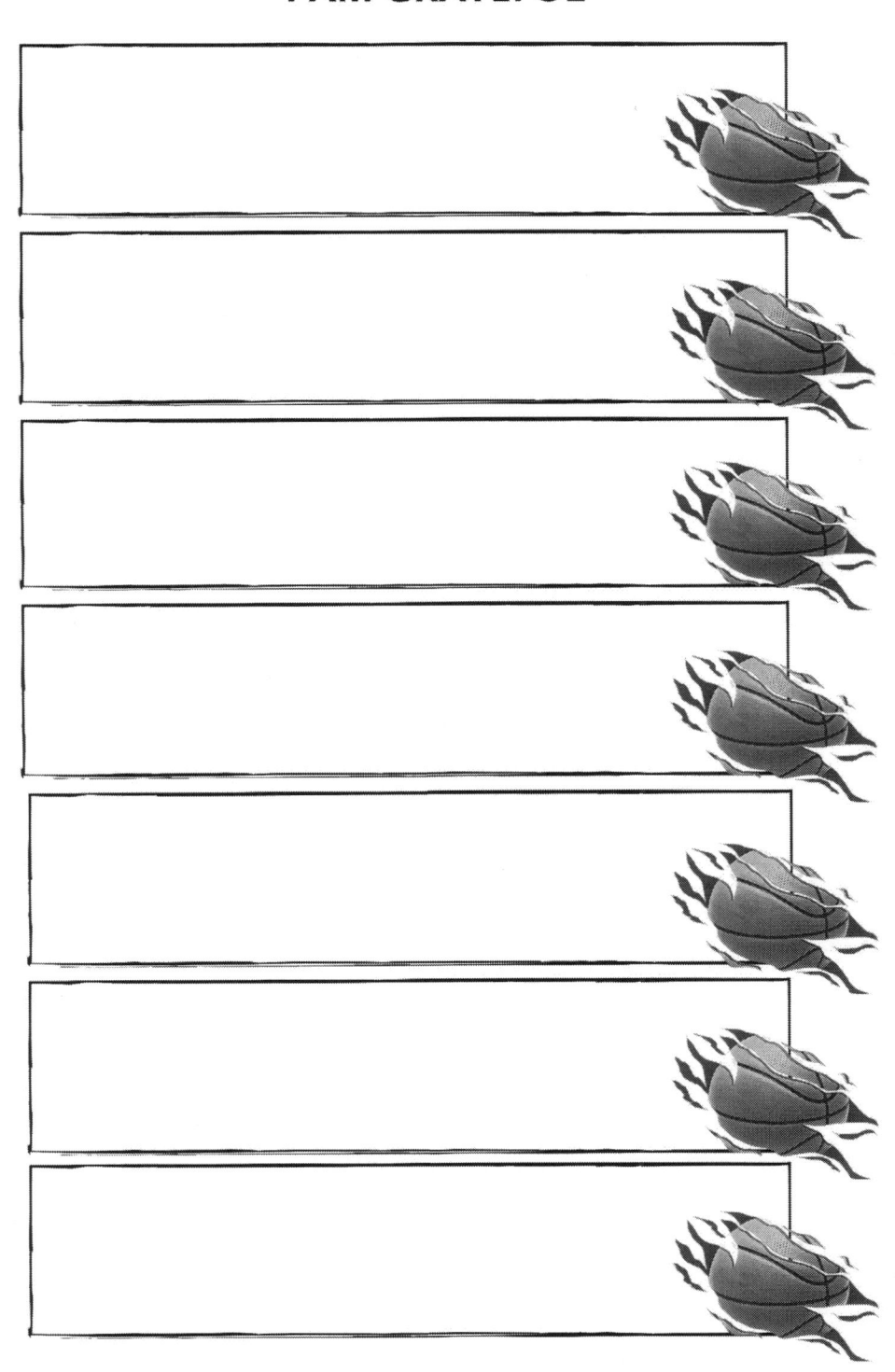

WEEK:_____   DATE:_____/_____/_____

THANK YOU

HAPPINESS never DECREASES BY BEING SHARED.

~ Gautama

QUARTERLY BENCHMARK GOALS

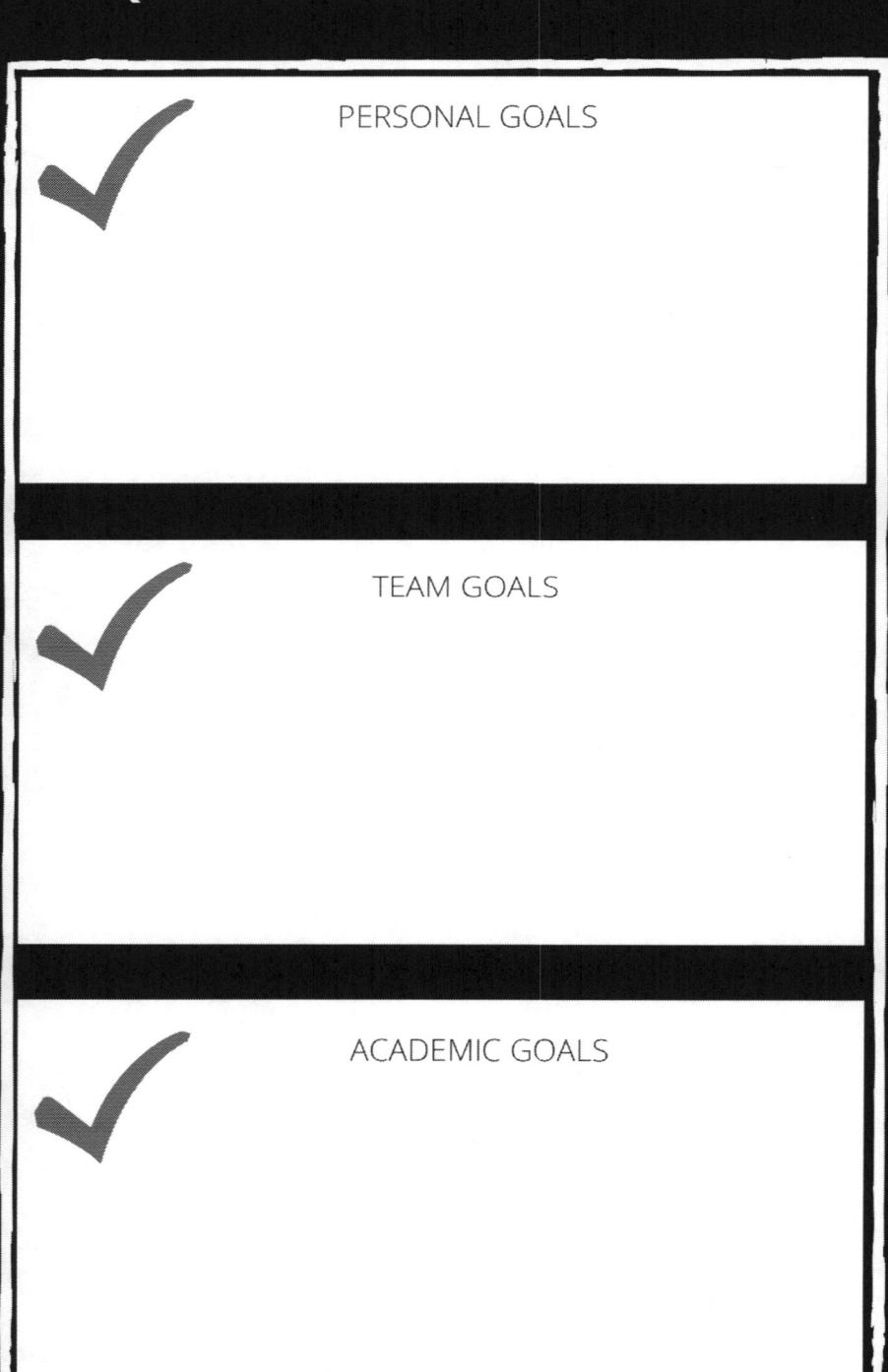

✓ PERSONAL GOALS

✓ TEAM GOALS

✓ ACADEMIC GOALS

WEEK:_____   DATE:_____/_____/_____

GOALS FOR THE MONTH

PERSONAL GOALS

TEAM GOALS

ACADEMIC GOALS

WEEK:_____   DATE:_____/_____/_____

HYDRATION

Week 1

Week 2

Week 3

Week 4

WEEK:_____   DATE:_____/_____/_____

Your results at games do not define your progress.

ACCOMPLISHMENTS I'M PROUD OF
_____
_____
_____

HOW I HELPED MY TEAMMATES
_____
_____
_____

FAVORITE BASKETBALL MOMENTS
_____
_____
_____

GETTING BUCKETS - PRACTICE NOTES AND AT-HOME GOALS
_____
_____

SHOOTING _____ ☐

DRIBBLING _____ ☐

SPRINTS _____ ☐

DISTANCE RUN _____ ☐

WEEK:_____ DATE:_____/_____/_____

Celebrate your accomplishments.

ACCOMPLISHMENTS I'M PROUD OF
_____
_____
_____

HOW I HELPED MY TEAMMATES
_____
_____
_____

FAVORITE BASKETBALL MOMENTS
_____
_____
_____

GETTING BUCKETS - PRACTICE NOTES AND AT-HOME GOALS
_____
_____

SHOOTING _____ ☐
DRIBBLING _____ ☐
SPRINTS _____ ☐
DISTANCE RUN _____ ☐

WEEK:_____ DATE:_____/_____/_____

Shine bright like the star that you are.

ACCOMPLISHMENTS I'M PROUD OF
_____
_____
_____

HOW I HELPED MY TEAMMATES
_____
_____
_____

FAVORITE BASKETBALL MOMENTS
_____
_____
_____

GETTING BUCKETS - PRACTICE NOTES AND AT-HOME GOALS
_____
_____

SHOOTING _____ ☐
DRIBBLING _____ ☐
SPRINTS _____ ☐
DISTANCE RUN _____ ☐

WEEK:_____ DATE:_____/_____/_____

Have faith in yourself and you will succeed.

ACCOMPLISHMENTS I'M PROUD OF
_____
_____
_____

HOW I HELPED MY TEAMMATES
_____
_____
_____

FAVORITE BASKETBALL MOMENTS
_____
_____
_____

GETTING BUCKETS - PRACTICE NOTES AND AT-HOME GOALS
_____
_____

SHOOTING _____ ☐
DRIBBLING _____ ☐
SPRINTS _____ ☐
DISTANCE RUN _____ ☐

WEEK:_____   DATE:_____/_____/_____

CELEBRATE MONTHLY PRACTICE WINS

Practice wins don't always have to be about learning new skills. Wins could be that you welcomed newcomers to your team and made them feel comfortable at a new club. Wins could be that you stayed positive even though you were having a hard day. Celebrating EVERY win is crucial to success and growth!

HOW DID MY SKILLS GROW?

_____
_____
_____
_____

HOW DID MY CHARACTER GROW?

_____
_____
_____
_____

HOW DID I GROW MENTALLY?

_____
_____
_____
_____

AFFIRMATIONS IN ACTION - visualize my goals as I say the statements below out loud.

When I did my _____, I felt _____
When my team _____, I felt _____

WEEK:_____ DATE:_____/_____/_____

MONTHLY REFLECTION

Sometimes life is two steps foward and one step back.

DID I REACH MY GOALS? If yes, what steps did I take to reach my goals? If not, what could I have done differently?

_____
_____
_____
_____

I WAS MOST POSITIVELY IMPACTED BY...

_____
_____
_____
_____

I POSITIVELY IMPACTED...

_____
_____
_____
_____

IN THE COMING WEEKS, I AM LOOKING FORWARD TO...

_____
_____
_____
_____

WEEK:_____   DATE:_____/_____/_____

VIDEO REVIEW NOTES

SUCCESSFUL MOMENTS WITHOUT THE BALL
_____
_____

SUCCESSFUL MOMENTS WITH THE BALL
_____
_____

MOMENTS I'D LIKE TO IMPROVE UPON
_____
_____

EFFORT LEVEL (1-5, 1 being the best effort)
Beginning _____ Middle _____ End _____

SUCCESSFUL MOMENTS WITHOUT THE BALL
_____
_____

SUCCESSFUL MOMENTS WITH THE BALL
_____
_____

MOMENTS I'D LIKE TO IMPROVE UPON
_____
_____

EFFORT LEVEL (1-5, 1 being the highest)
Beginning _____ Middle _____ End _____

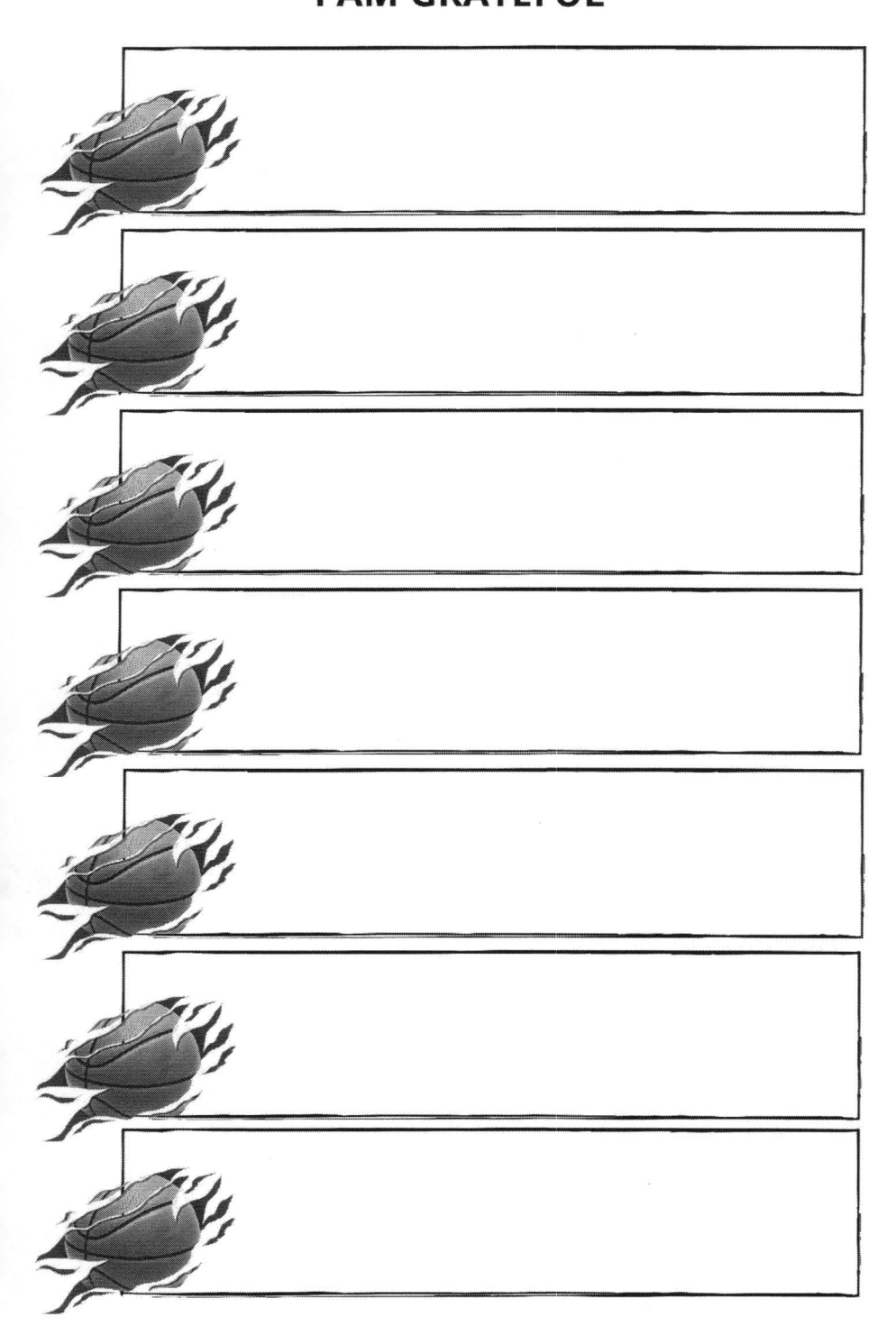

WEEK:_____   DATE:_____/_____/_____

I AM GRATEFUL

WEEK:_____   DATE:_____/_____/_____

THANK YOU

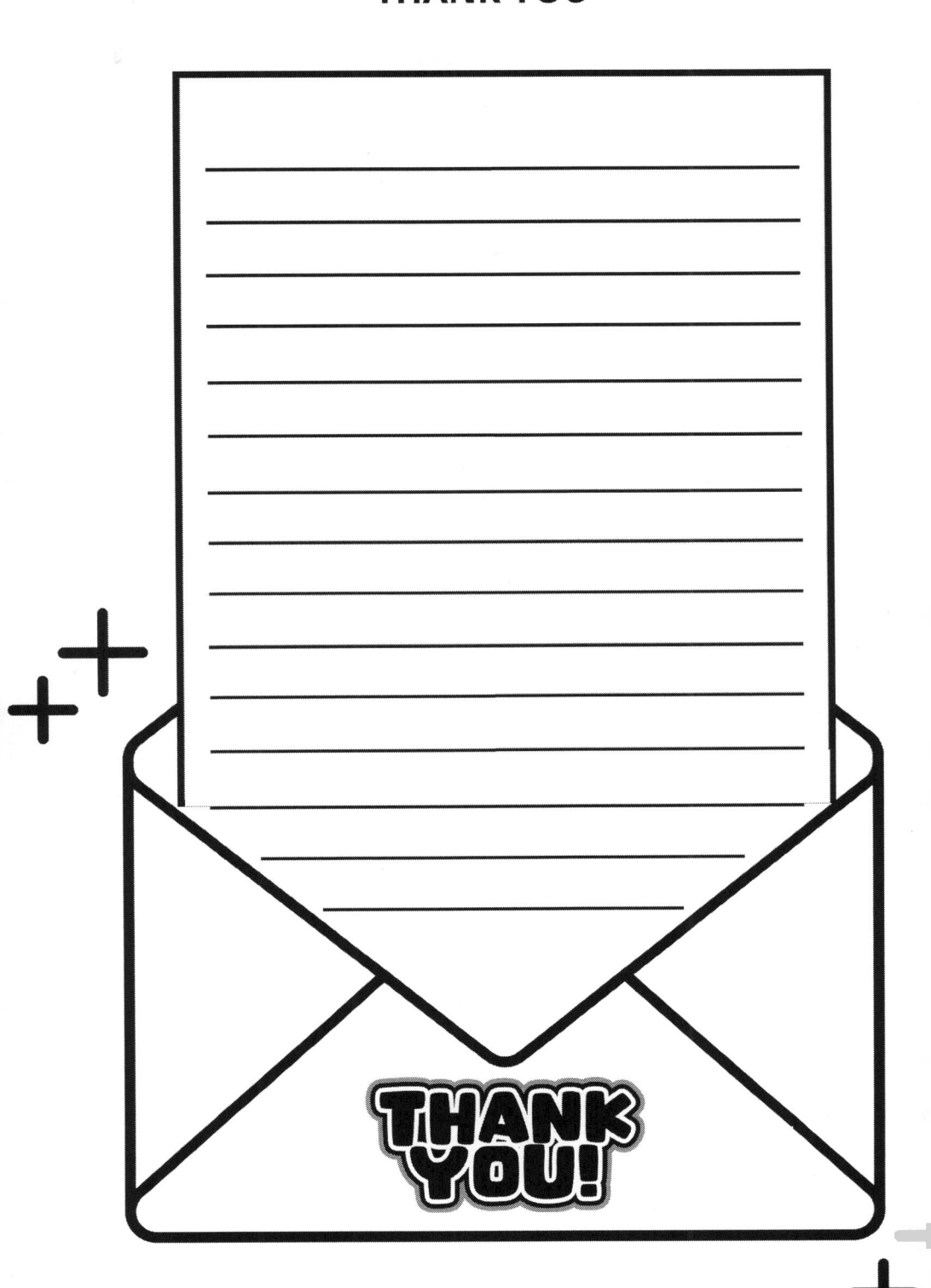

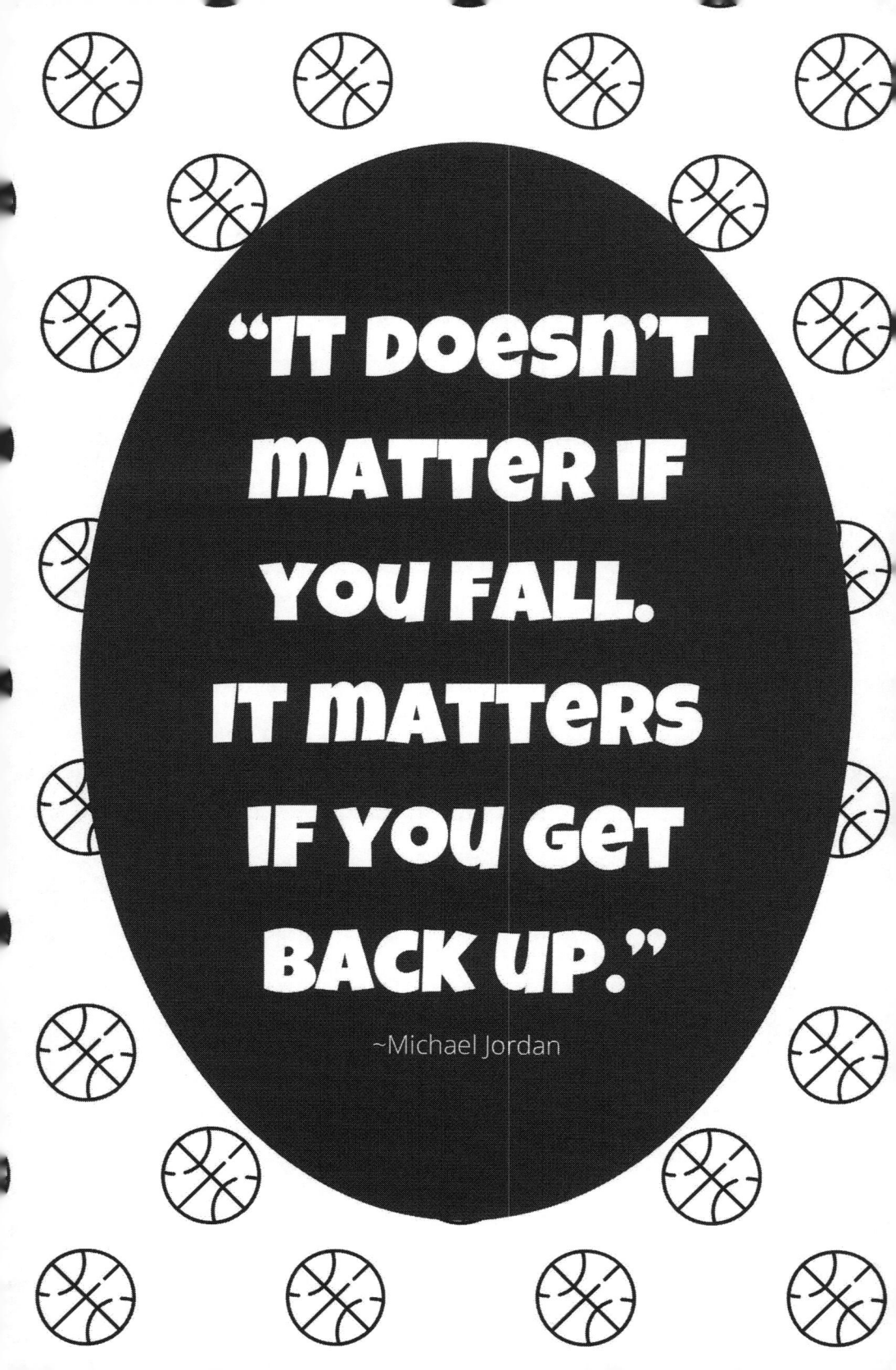

"IT DOESN'T MATTER IF YOU FALL. IT MATTERS IF YOU GET BACK UP."

~Michael Jordan

WEEK:_____   DATE:_____/_____/_____

GOALS FOR THE MONTH

PERSONAL GOALS

TEAM GOALS

ACADEMIC GOALS

WEEK:_____ DATE:_____/_____/_____

HYDRATION

Week 1

Week 2

Week 3

Week 4

WEEK:_____ DATE:_____/_____/_____

Don't just do the work when others are watching.

ACCOMPLISHMENTS I'M PROUD OF
_____
_____
_____

HOW I HELPED MY TEAMMATES
_____
_____
_____

FAVORITE BASKETBALL MOMENTS
_____
_____
_____

GETTING BUCKETS - PRACTICE NOTES AND AT-HOME GOALS
_____
_____

SHOOTING _____ ☐
DRIBBLING _____ ☐
SPRINTS _____ ☐
DISTANCE RUN _____ ☐

WEEK:_____   DATE:_____/_____/_____

Stay focused on your goals.

ACCOMPLISHMENTS I'M PROUD OF
_____
_____
_____

HOW I HELPED MY TEAMMATES
_____
_____
_____

FAVORITE BASKETBALL MOMENTS
_____
_____
_____

GETTING BUCKETS - PRACTICE NOTES AND AT-HOME GOALS
_____
_____

SHOOTING _____

DRIBBLING _____

SPRINTS _____

DISTANCE RUN _____

WEEK:_____ DATE:_____/_____/_____

Don't be afraid to dream big.

ACCOMPLISHMENTS I'M PROUD OF
_____
_____
_____

HOW I HELPED MY TEAMMATES
_____
_____
_____

FAVORITE BASKETBALL MOMENTS
_____
_____
_____

GETTING BUCKETS - PRACTICE NOTES AND AT-HOME GOALS
_____
_____

SHOOTING _____ ☐
DRIBBLING _____ ☐
SPRINTS   _____ ☐
DISTANCE RUN _____ ☐

WEEK:_____   DATE:_____/_____/_____

Teammates can be the best friends.

ACCOMPLISHMENTS I'M PROUD OF
_____
_____
_____

HOW I HELPED MY TEAMMATES
_____
_____
_____

FAVORITE BASKETBALL MOMENTS
_____
_____
_____

GETTING BUCKETS - PRACTICE NOTES AND AT-HOME GOALS
_____
_____

SHOOTING _____ ☐
DRIBBLING _____ ☐
SPRINTS   _____ ☐
DISTANCE RUN _____ ☐

WEEK:_____   DATE:_____/_____/_____

CELEBRATE MONTHLY PRACTICE WINS

Practice wins don't always have to be about learning new skills. Wins could be that you welcomed newcomers to your team and made them feel comfortable at a new club. Wins could be that you stayed positive even though you were having a hard day. Celebrating EVERY win is crucial to success and growth!

HOW DID MY SKILLS GROW?

_____
_____
_____
_____

HOW DID MY CHARACTER GROW?

_____
_____
_____
_____

HOW DID I GROW MENTALLY?

_____
_____
_____
_____

AFFIRMATIONS IN ACTION - visualize my goals as I say the statements below out loud.

When I did my _____, I felt _____
When my team _____, I felt _____

WEEK:_____   DATE:_____/_____/_____

MONTHLY REFLECTION

The greatest fault is not being conscious of your own faults.

DID I REACH MY GOALS? If yes, what steps did I take to reach my goals? If not, what could I have done differently?

_____
_____
_____
_____

I WAS MOST POSITIVELY IMPACTED BY...

_____
_____
_____
_____

I POSITIVELY IMPACTED...

_____
_____
_____
_____

IN THE COMING WEEKS, I AM LOOKING FORWARD TO...

_____
_____
_____
_____

WEEK:_____   DATE:_____/_____/_____

VIDEO REVIEW NOTES

SUCCESSFUL MOMENTS WITHOUT THE BALL
_____
_____

SUCCESSFUL MOMENTS WITH THE BALL
_____
_____

MOMENTS I'D LIKE TO IMPROVE UPON
_____
_____

EFFORT LEVEL (1-5, 1 being the best effort)
Beginning _____ Middle _____ End _____

SUCCESSFUL MOMENTS WITHOUT THE BALL
_____
_____

SUCCESSFUL MOMENTS WITH THE BALL
_____
_____

MOMENTS I'D LIKE TO IMPROVE UPON
_____
_____

EFFORT LEVEL (1-5, 1 being the highest)
Beginning _____ Middle _____ End _____

WEEK:_____   DATE:_____/_____/_____

I AM GRATEFUL

WEEK:_____   DATE:_____/_____/_____

THANK YOU

WEEK:_____   DATE:_____/_____/_____

GOALS FOR THE MONTH

PERSONAL GOALS

TEAM GOALS

ACADEMIC GOALS

WEEK:_____   DATE:_____/_____/_____

HYDRATION

Week 1

Week 2

Week 3

Week 4

WEEK:_____   DATE:_____/_____/_____

The lessons along the way are the real prize.

ACCOMPLISHMENTS I'M PROUD OF
_____
_____
_____

HOW I HELPED MY TEAMMATES
_____
_____
_____

FAVORITE BASKETBALL MOMENTS
_____
_____
_____

GETTING BUCKETS - PRACTICE NOTES AND AT-HOME GOALS
_____
_____

SHOOTING   _____ ☐
DRIBBLING   _____ ☐
SPRINTS   _____ ☐
DISTANCE RUN _____ ☐

WEEK:_____ DATE:_____/_____/_____

There is never a time to stop learning.

ACCOMPLISHMENTS I'M PROUD OF
_____
_____
_____

HOW I HELPED MY TEAMMATES
_____
_____
_____

FAVORITE BASKETBALL MOMENTS
_____
_____
_____

GETTING BUCKETS - PRACTICE NOTES AND AT-HOME GOALS
_____
_____

SHOOTING _____ ☐

DRIBBLING _____ ☐

SPRINTS _____ ☐

DISTANCE RUN _____ ☐

WEEK:_____   DATE:_____/_____/_____

Put in the work and the results will come.

ACCOMPLISHMENTS I'M PROUD OF
_____
_____
_____

HOW I HELPED MY TEAMMATES
_____
_____
_____

FAVORITE BASKETBALL MOMENTS
_____
_____
_____

GETTING BUCKETS - PRACTICE NOTES AND AT-HOME GOALS
_____
_____

SHOOTING   _____ ☐
DRIBBLING   _____ ☐
SPRINTS   _____ ☐
DISTANCE RUN _____ ☐

WEEK:_____   DATE:_____/_____/_____

You're on your OWN journey, don't compare yourself to others.

ACCOMPLISHMENTS I'M PROUD OF

_____
_____
_____

HOW I HELPED MY TEAMMATES

_____
_____
_____

FAVORITE BASKETBALL MOMENTS

_____
_____
_____

GETTING BUCKETS - PRACTICE NOTES AND AT-HOME GOALS

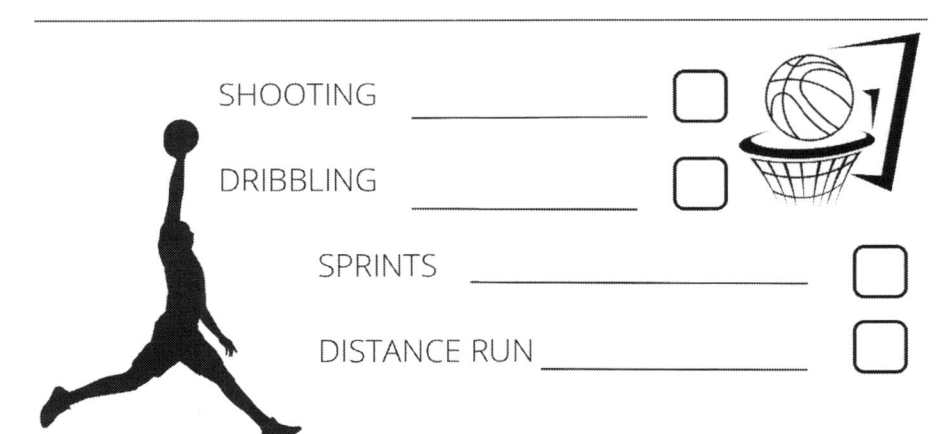

_____
_____

SHOOTING _____ ☐

DRIBBLING _____ ☐

SPRINTS _____ ☐

DISTANCE RUN _____ ☐

WEEK:_____   DATE:_____/_____/_____

Reflect on your year and enjoy the growth.

ACCOMPLISHMENTS I'M PROUD OF
_____
_____
_____

HOW I HELPED MY TEAMMATES
_____
_____
_____

FAVORITE BASKETBALLO MOMENTS
_____
_____
_____

GETTING BUCKETS - PRACTICE NOTES AND AT-HOME GOALS
_____
_____

SHOOTING   _____   ☐
DRIBBLING _____   ☐
SPRINTS   _____   ☐
DISTANCE RUN _____ ☐

WEEK:_____   DATE:_____/_____/_____

CELEBRATE MONTHLY PRACTICE WINS

Practice wins don't always have to be about learning new skills. Wins could be that you welcomed newcomers to your team and made them feel comfortable at a new club. Wins could be that you stayed positive even though you were having a hard day. Celebrating EVERY win is crucial to success and growth!

HOW DID MY SKILLS GROW?

_____
_____
_____
_____

HOW DID MY CHARACTER GROW?

_____
_____
_____
_____

HOW DID I GROW MENTALLY?

_____
_____
_____
_____

AFFIRMATIONS IN ACTION - visualize my goals as I say the statements below out loud.

When I did my _____, I felt _____
When my team _____, I felt _____

WEEK:_____ DATE:_____/_____/_____

MONTHLY REFLECTION

Learn from the past to gain perspective on the future.

DID I REACH MY GOALS? If yes, what steps did I take to reach my goals? If not, what could I have done differently?

_____
_____
_____
_____

I WAS MOST POSITIVELY IMPACTED BY...

_____
_____
_____
_____

I POSITIVELY IMPACTED...

_____
_____
_____
_____

IN THE COMING WEEKS, I AM LOOKING FORWARD TO...

_____
_____
_____
_____

WEEK:_____   DATE:_____/_____/_____

VIDEO REVIEW NOTES

SUCCESSFUL MOMENTS WITHOUT THE BALL

_____

_____

SUCCESSFUL MOMENTS WITH THE BALL

_____

_____

MOMENTS I'D LIKE TO IMPROVE UPON

_____

_____

EFFORT LEVEL (1-5, 1 being the best effort)
Beginning _____ Middle _____ End _____

SUCCESSFUL MOMENTS WITHOUT THE BALL

_____

_____

SUCCESSFUL MOMENTS WITH THE BALL

_____

_____

MOMENTS I'D LIKE TO IMPROVE UPON

_____

_____

EFFORT LEVEL (1-5, 1 being the highest)
Beginning _____ Middle _____ End _____

WEEK:_____ DATE:_____/_____/_____

I AM GRATEFUL

WEEK:_____ DATE:_____/_____/_____

THANK YOU

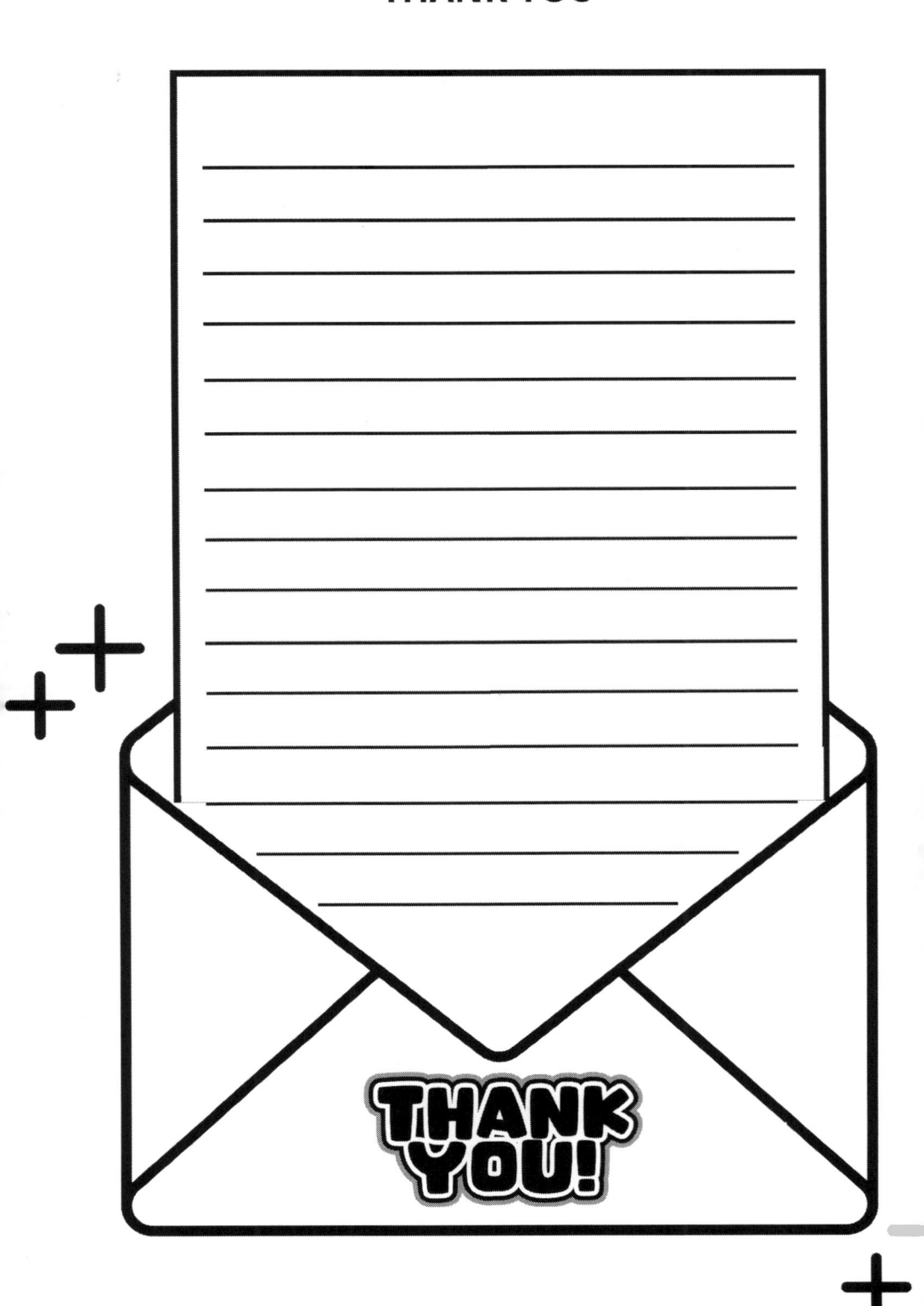

YOU ONLY GET OUT OF BALL WHAT YOU GIVE TO BALL.

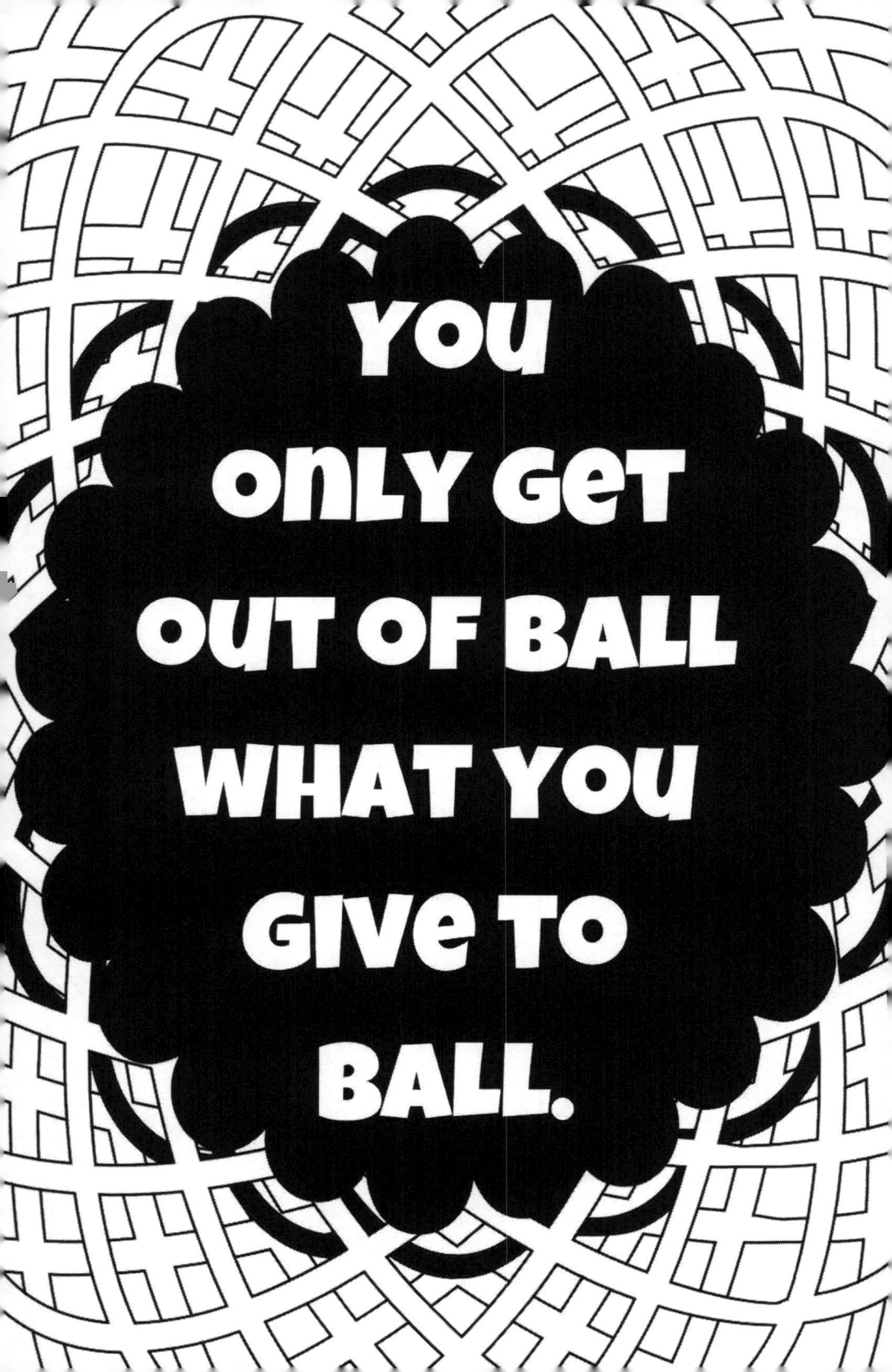

GAME STATS AND MEMORIES

EVENT NAME: _____

CITY: _____ DATE: _____

TEAM STATS | PLAYER STATS

TEAM STATS		PLAYER STATS	
SHOTS	_____	SHOTS	_____
POINTS	_____	POINTS	_____
FT ATTEMPT	_____	FT ATTEMPT	_____
FT POINTS	_____	FT POINTS	_____
3P ATTEMPT	_____	3P ATTEMPT	_____
3P POINTS	_____	3P POINTS	_____
REBOUNDS	_____	REBOUNDS	_____

NOTES _____
_____
_____

NEW FRIENDS | FUN TIMES

GAME STATS AND MEMORIES

EVENT NAME: _____

CITY: _____ DATE: _____

TEAM STATS | PLAYER STATS

TEAM STATS		PLAYER STATS	
SHOTS	_____	SHOTS	_____
POINTS	_____	POINTS	_____
FT ATTEMPT	_____	FT ATTEMPT	_____
FT POINTS	_____	FT POINTS	_____
3P ATTEMPT	_____	3P ATTEMPT	_____
3P POINTS	_____	3P POINTS	_____
REBOUNDS	_____	REBOUNDS	_____

NOTES _____
_____
_____

NEW FRIENDS | FUN TIMES

GAME STATS AND MEMORIES

EVENT NAME: _____

CITY: _____ DATE: _____

TEAM STATS | PLAYER STATS

TEAM STATS		PLAYER STATS	
SHOTS	_____	SHOTS	_____
POINTS	_____	POINTS	_____
FT ATTEMPT	_____	FT ATTEMPT	_____
FT POINTS	_____	FT POINTS	_____
3P ATTEMPT	_____	3P ATTEMPT	_____
3P POINTS	_____	3P POINTS	_____
REBOUNDS	_____	REBOUNDS	_____

NOTES _____
_____
_____

NEW FRIENDS

_____
_____
_____
_____

FUN TIMES

_____
_____
_____
_____

GAME STATS AND MEMORIES

EVENT NAME: _____

CITY: _____ DATE: _____

TEAM STATS | PLAYER STATS

TEAM STATS		PLAYER STATS	
SHOTS	_____	SHOTS	_____
POINTS	_____	POINTS	_____
FT ATTEMPT	_____	FT ATTEMPT	_____
FT POINTS	_____	FT POINTS	_____
3P ATTEMPT	_____	3P ATTEMPT	_____
3P POINTS	_____	3P POINTS	_____
REBOUNDS	_____	REBOUNDS	_____

NOTES _____
_____
_____

NEW FRIENDS | FUN TIMES

GAME STATS AND MEMORIES

EVENT NAME: _____

CITY: _____ DATE: _____

TEAM STATS | PLAYER STATS

TEAM STATS		PLAYER STATS	
SHOTS	_____	SHOTS	_____
POINTS	_____	POINTS	_____
FT ATTEMPT	_____	FT ATTEMPT	_____
FT POINTS	_____	FT POINTS	_____
3P ATTEMPT	_____	3P ATTEMPT	_____
3P POINTS	_____	3P POINTS	_____
REBOUNDS	_____	REBOUNDS	_____

NOTES _____
_____
_____

NEW FRIENDS

_____
_____
_____

FUN TIMES

_____
_____
_____

GAME STATS AND MEMORIES

EVENT NAME: _____

CITY: _____ DATE: _____

TEAM STATS | PLAYER STATS

TEAM STATS		PLAYER STATS	
SHOTS	_____	SHOTS	_____
POINTS	_____	POINTS	_____
FT ATTEMPT	_____	FT ATTEMPT	_____
FT POINTS	_____	FT POINTS	_____
3P ATTEMPT	_____	3P ATTEMPT	_____
3P POINTS	_____	3P POINTS	_____
REBOUNDS	_____	REBOUNDS	_____

NOTES _____
_____
_____

NEW FRIENDS

_____
_____
_____
_____

FUN TIMES

_____
_____
_____
_____

GAME STATS AND MEMORIES

EVENT NAME: _____

CITY: _____ DATE: _____

TEAM STATS | PLAYER STATS

TEAM STATS		PLAYER STATS	
SHOTS	_____	SHOTS	_____
POINTS	_____	POINTS	_____
FT ATTEMPT	_____	FT ATTEMPT	_____
FT POINTS	_____	FT POINTS	_____
3P ATTEMPT	_____	3P ATTEMPT	_____
3P POINTS	_____	3P POINTS	_____
REBOUNDS	_____	REBOUNDS	_____

NOTES _____
_____
_____

NEW FRIENDS

FUN TIMES

GAME STATS AND MEMORIES

EVENT NAME: _____

CITY: _____ DATE: _____

TEAM STATS | PLAYER STATS

TEAM STATS		PLAYER STATS	
SHOTS	_____	SHOTS	_____
POINTS	_____	POINTS	_____
FT ATTEMPT	_____	FT ATTEMPT	_____
FT POINTS	_____	FT POINTS	_____
3P ATTEMPT	_____	3P ATTEMPT	_____
3P POINTS	_____	3P POINTS	_____
REBOUNDS	_____	REBOUNDS	_____

NOTES _____
_____
_____

NEW FRIENDS

_____
_____
_____
_____

FUN TIMES

_____
_____
_____
_____

GAME STATS AND MEMORIES

EVENT NAME: _____

CITY: _____ DATE: _____

TEAM STATS | PLAYER STATS

TEAM STATS		PLAYER STATS	
SHOTS	_____	SHOTS	_____
POINTS	_____	POINTS	_____
FT ATTEMPT	_____	FT ATTEMPT	_____
FT POINTS	_____	FT POINTS	_____
3P ATTEMPT	_____	3P ATTEMPT	_____
3P POINTS	_____	3P POINTS	_____
REBOUNDS	_____	REBOUNDS	_____

NOTES _____
_____
_____

NEW FRIENDS

_____
_____
_____
_____

FUN TIMES

_____
_____
_____
_____

GAME STATS AND MEMORIES

EVENT NAME: _____

CITY: _____ DATE: _____

TEAM STATS | PLAYER STATS

TEAM STATS		PLAYER STATS	
SHOTS	_____	SHOTS	_____
POINTS	_____	POINTS	_____
FT ATTEMPT	_____	FT ATTEMPT	_____
FT POINTS	_____	FT POINTS	_____
3P ATTEMPT	_____	3P ATTEMPT	_____
3P POINTS	_____	3P POINTS	_____
REBOUNDS	_____	REBOUNDS	_____

NOTES _____
_____
_____

NEW FRIENDS | FUN TIMES

GAME STATS AND MEMORIES

EVENT NAME: _____

CITY: _____ DATE: _____

TEAM STATS | PLAYER STATS

TEAM STATS		PLAYER STATS	
SHOTS	_____	SHOTS	_____
POINTS	_____	POINTS	_____
FT ATTEMPT	_____	FT ATTEMPT	_____
FT POINTS	_____	FT POINTS	_____
3P ATTEMPT	_____	3P ATTEMPT	_____
3P POINTS	_____	3P POINTS	_____
REBOUNDS	_____	REBOUNDS	_____

NOTES _____
_____
_____

NEW FRIENDS | FUN TIMES

ACKNOWLEDGMENTS

To all the basketball coaches and club owners, thank you for sharing your passion for sports. Thank you for making the sacrifices necessary to provide safe and wonderful learning environments for all kids who want to play basketball. I know the grind, and I appreciate all that you do.

To my former teachers, coaches, and instructors thank you for everything you taught me through the years. I wouldn't be who I am today without your guidance and mentorship.

To my husband, thank you. Thank you for being supportive of my crazy ideas and ventures, for late-night chats, and for always encouraging me.

To my children, I love you more than any words can express. Everything I do is for you.

To my former athletes, thank you for inspiring me daily to be a better mentor, teacher, and coach. I am so proud of each and every one of you.

To my friends, brothers, sisters, nieces, and nephews, thank you for being the best. I am so lucky to say you are my friends and my family. Your love and support mean the world to me.

ABOUT THE AUTHOR

S.R. Fabrico

S.R. Fabrico is an award-winning author whose literary talents have captivated readers worldwide. With her debut novel, The Secrets We Conceal, she has emerged as a rising star in the literary realm.

With a remarkable 25-plus-year career in business, marketing, and sports, S.R. Fabrico brings a unique perspective to her writing. As a World Champion Dance Coach and esteemed speaker, she infuses her stories with passion and insight.

Helping athletes grow as young adults has always been my passion. She is honored to provide a journal for young athletes that may positively assist them along their journeys.

Residing in Tennessee with her husband and children, S.R. Fabrico continues to create novels and athletic journals.

Let's get social @srfabrico_author

Interested in setting up a fundraiser or a bulk order discount?. Email srfabricoauthor@gmail.com.

Stay up to date on recent news and information and subscribe to her newsletter at www.srfabrico.com

Subscribe to S.R. Fabrico's newsletter

My Basketball Journal is available for teams and clubs at bulk order discounts!

Email srfabricoauthor@gmail.com

OTHER WORKS BY S.R. FABRICO

My Dance Journal

My Cheer Journal

My Gymnastics Journal

My Swim Journal

My Volleyball Journal

My Soccer Journal

The Firefly Journal
A journal for woman

Would you like a My Journal in a sport that isn't available?
Email srfabricoauthor@gmail.com

Made in the USA
Las Vegas, NV
08 April 2025

17db992a-4668-4e67-81f5-e03f9734716cR01